Alzheimer's disease is
"the long good-bye."
For Mom it was twenty years.
She died in 2000.
People often ask,
"How did you deal with it?"
It was one day at a time,
thanking God for
ordinary things...

like a new doll, an old purse,
pink nail polish, a red barn,
a Dairy Queen®, and butterscotch sundaes.

Mom's story is upbeat and personal
with a sense of humor and the gift of hope.

- Virginia McCone
Author ~ Speaker ~ Columnist

"Butterscotch Sundaes...
is simply and beautifully written."
Jolene Brackey, author of *Creating Moments of Joy*

"This is a must-read book for anyone
seeking an understanding of Alzheimer's."
Lois Thompson Bartholomew, author of *The White Dove*

"A wonderful mother-daughter story...
rarer than anything you can imagine."
Bill Charlesworth, Professor Emeritus
Human Development, University of Minnesota

ISBN 0-9728201-0-8

9 780972 820103

Butterscotch Sundaes

My Mom's Story

of

Alzheimer's

Virginia McCone

Autumn Sparrow Press
2003 Publication

Jan. 17, 2004

Cherish your butterscotch moments!

Vin Cone

**Printed with permission the poem, "I Wonder"
by Ruth Harms Calkin**

Unless otherwise noted as KJV from the King James Version, Scripture references are from the HOLY BIBLE; NEW INTERNATIONAL VERSION *Copyright 1973, 1978, 1984 by International Bible Society. Used by permission of Zondervan Publishing House. All rights reserved.

Printed by Master Graphics of New Ulm, Minnesota.

Cover design and back cover photo by John Judkins of Stassen Photography, Tracy/Springfield, Minnesota.

How to order this book! Contact:

 Autumn Sparrow Press
12598 Magnolia Ave.
Sanborn, MN 56083
Phone 507-723-5138
website www.sodhouse.org *click on author*

Author's Notes

To my children, Christy, Benton, Charlie, Steve, and Tom, thank you for listening to my stories over the years. To my son Steve, I especially owe gratitude for occasionally interrupting me by saying, "Mom, does this story have a point?" Because of you, I learned how to have a point and how to come to the point. Thank you for tolerating the crazy lifestyle of a writer, speaker, and newspaper columnist.

* * * MOM

To my husband, Stan, you have always been my source of inspiration and encouragement. I admire and appreciate you more than you will ever know.

* * * Your wife, Virginia

Thank you to my proof readers, Anne Bausch, Marlene Durscher, Barb Sommers, Glenn and Linda Letellier.

Thank you to my manuscript readers:
Ann Getting, Michelle Hall, Susan Manda, Dawn Vander Weide, Doris Weber, Mary and Wayne Pauluk, Barb Purves, Marlys Vanderwerf, Barb Keith, Johanna Wilson, Rose Landa, Lisa Bausch, Shelly Bausch, Connie Klaus, Heidi McCone, Tanya Lyon, Lois Brompton, Dorie Gill, Jolene Brackey, Lois Bartholomew, and Bill Charlesworth.

Thank you Steve Lawrence, General Manager at Master Graphics! Thank you Nickie Sabo, Graphic Designer at Master Graphics, for all your help with the Graphic Designs!

Thank you Crosby Sommers, talented composer, concert pianist, and my dear friend.

Somewhere between the bitter and the sweet of life
is the bittersweet,
the memory of my mother eating a butterscotch sundae.

* * * *Virginia McCone*

Ethel Mae Bausch

1910-2000   1995 Photo

Dedication

To a pretty white-haired lady
with her chocolate chip eyes
and her butterscotch sundae smile.

As the chapters unfold and the story is told,
ordinary things become extraordinary.

* * * Virginia McCone

Chapter Titles

Chapter One   Preview of the Book 9

Chapter Two   Early Signs on the Farm 13

Chapter Three   Warning Signs on the Prairie 20

Chapter Four   Bright Colors and Ice Cream Sundaes . . . 28

Chapter Five   Hallucinations of Aunt Alice 36

Chapter Six   My Clothesline Decision 43

Chapter Seven   A Special Home for Mom 50

Chapter Eight   Paying Mom's Bills 60

Chapter Nine   Creating Special Moments. 64

Chapter Ten   A Second Childhood. 71

Chapter Eleven   The Doll 82

Chapter Twelve   Pink Nail Polish 87

Chapter Thirteen   Learning Detachment 93

Chapter Fourteen   Mom Waves Good-bye 98

Chapter Fifteen   The Valley of the Shadow 103

Chapter Sixteen   The Purple Tide 112

Chapter Seventeen   A Smile For Her Escort 115

Chapter Eighteen   My Final Walk with Mom 117

Chapter Nineteen   A Snowflake's Design 120

Chapter Twenty   Remembering Mom 124

Chapter Twenty-One   Life Goes On 132

To lose someone twice is not an easy road.

* * * *Virginia McCone*

Preview of the Book
Chapter One

I don't know why Mom loved butterscotch sundaes. She just did. Her eyes twinkled when she tasted its brown sugar sweetness. Each spoonful was savored and enjoyed to make it last longer. When it was the last spoonful, she scraped the bottom and sides of the dish to make sure she hadn't missed any. Then she smiled and said in her low soothing voice, "Mmmm . . . that was so good."

My husband often teased her about loving ice cream. He'd say to her, "Ethel, someday you're going to turn into a butterscotch sundae." She would smile at him, shrug her shoulders, and tell us her ice cream story. "My dad used to tease me about loving ice cream. One day he dared me to put ketchup on my ice cream to see if I could still eat it. And I did."

Eating ice cream always made Mom feel chilly, so she quickly found her sweater on the back of her chair and snuggled into it. "Grandma, would you still love eating ice cream, if you were sitting on top of a huge snowbank on a cold snowy day?" her twelve- year-old grandson asked her in a challenging sort of way.

"Sure I would, Tom. I'd eat it anytime and anywhere. Did I ever tell you my ice cream story? My dad used to tease me about loving ice cream. One day he dared me to put ketchup on my ice cream to see if I could still eat it. And I did."

Dessert time was over, and we cleared the dishes from the kitchen table. Mom put the jar of butterscotch topping into the refrigerator while Tom covered the ice cream pail and shoved it into the freezer. As Tom was leaving the kitchen, his grandmother spoke to him again. "Tom, did I ever tell you my ice cream story? My dad used to tease me about loving ice cream. One day he dared me to put ketchup on my ice cream to see if I could still eat it. And I did."

When Mom finished telling us the same story for a third time, I put my arms around her, hugged her and invited her to go for a walk with me. She reached for her walking stick, and we went outside. Mom had repeated her ice cream story using the same gestures, the same words, and the same expressions. Each time, it was as if she were telling it to us for the very first time. We could see that Mom had a memory problem. Now what…?

This is the book that answers the question, "Now what…?" It's the story of my mother and her twenty-year journey with Alzheimer's disease. It's about real people in a real life situation with no need to enlarge the details because the truth is enough. It's the story of our family facing a diagnosis we didn't want to hear, one that for years we denied by making excuses for the symptoms. It's about changing plans. Like any other family, we were making plans for the future, but Alzheimer's changed our plans, and we had to take a journey, one that we never would have chosen to take.

It's a story about our family's love for one another and how it deepened as we took the journey together. Through many emotional highs and lows, we learned to trust God when faith was stretched more than it had ever been. We found God to be very personal when He did some amazing things for us along the way. He used ordinary things in extraordinary ways. A new doll. An old purse. Pink nail polish. A red barn. A Dairy Queen. And of course, butterscotch sundaes.

This is the story of how our family tried to keep Mom at home even when her condition worsened. A butterscotch sundae at the Dairy Queen was more than an ice cream treat, and the wearing of brightly colored clothing was more than a fashion statement. It's about our family making every effort to keep Mom's mind from failing.

It's the story of Alzheimer's and the progressive stages of the disease. It's the story of the aging process as it takes an unexpected twist, a return to childhood when the mind, the personality, and the bodily functions go in reverse. Help is needed to dress, to walk, to talk, and to eat. Gradually, it becomes a story of diapers, bibs, spoon feedings, wheelchairs and geri chairs.

This is the story of how our family faced the changes in Mom's condition. It's about being creative, upbeat, and having a sense of humor. It's about finding ways to communicate when words are no longer possible. It's making the best of things when things get worse. It's learning the lessons Mom taught us in return, like making the most of the present moment because when it's gone, it's gone.

This is the story of St. John Lutheran Home, a special home for Mom, when she needed the type of care we could no longer give her. For nearly five years, Mom lived in a facility that treated her with utmost dignity, a place where her caregivers were not just doing their job, but they were also involved in a ministry to the elderly.

Ultimately, it's a story about death, yet a positive one because it was a victory over death. The final day was a long day, and the tension mounted as her breathing stopped, paused, and started again. At 2:10 on a Sunday afternoon, she was released from her body to be with the Lord.

The funeral and burial services were small and private as our family gathered to remember her as she was in the days before Alzheimer's took us on the journey. The memory was vague because the journey had been so long. What was she like before all of this happened to her? We looked through stacks of photo albums to see pictures of her, hoping to restore the image of what she used to be. Then someone reminisced how she loved to eat ice cream, and once again our family could visualize Mom seated with us at a table in an ice cream parlor.

Her brown eyes sparkle when she tastes the rich sweetness of the butterscotch topping. Each spoonful is savored and enjoyed to make it last longer. When it's the last spoonful, she scrapes the sides and the bottom of the glass dish to make sure she hasn't missed any. As she dabs the corner of each side of her mouth with her cloth napkin, she smiles and says in her low soothing voice, "Mmmm . . . that was so good."

Butterscotch sundaes. Precious memories.

Ethel Mae Bausch, my mother, was a very special woman. As her daughter, I am honored to write her story. Here's the book that I wished our family could have had as we took the Alzheimer's journey. It's an intimate look into the illness called "the long good-bye." Yet it's a story of hope.

As I tell her story, I invite you to get close to me, real close to me, as if you were sitting next to me on my big brown sofa in my living room. You will find me to be open and personal. As the story unfolds, I will share my struggles, my denial, my guilt, my joys, and my faith. But I must warn you I'm not going to tell it in chronological order. I will start near the beginning, and I will close just a little past the end of the journey. But in the middle, I will wander a bit. Storytellers can do that, you know.

Mom's story begins with the early stage of Alzheimer's. She is sitting on a fallen tree stump in a wooded area on a farm in Nebraska. Let me take you there now.

Early Signs on the Farm
Chapter Two

She was sitting on a log in the woods waiting for someone to find her. For reasons unknown to her, she couldn't find her way home. A fallen tree stump made a comfortable chair for her as she waited. She wasn't crying nor was she upset. She was just confused and perplexed.

That morning she had gone for her usual walk to the near-by town of Waterbury. The farm dogs, Bingo and Perky, had started out with her, but at some point they lost interest and chased a rabbit into the pasture and over the hill. She continued walking without the dogs because she loved walking. Her walks kept her healthy and spry for a woman of seventy-three. Going to town meant having coffee and fellowship with her friends Clara, Cecelia, Peggy or Bertha.

When coffee time was over that morning as she headed back to the farm, she was happy and smiling, and she waved at an occasional car or truck passing by her on the gravel road. Suddenly, she was confused because she thought she was walking on the road to her grandpa Pitman's farm. She knew it should be a straight road, but instead it had curves and hills.

Her uneasiness made her turn around and head toward town again. Instead of finding her grandfather's farm, she decided to look for her father's butcher's shop. It should be easy to find, after all she worked in the shop on weekends. Not only was it a meat market, but it also was a hamburger shop that served huge hamburgers on homemade buns with pickles and onions, all for the price of fifteen cents.

When she reached town again, she looked and looked, walked and walked, but she couldn't find her father's meat market. Finally, she stopped in front of the post office. When she read the sign above the door, Waterbury, Nebraska 68785, she realized she was in Nebraska and not in Illinois. Then she quietly and sheepishly reached inside the pockets of her navy jacket and looked for some letters to mail. None. She didn't have any letters to mail that day. She wondered what she was doing there.

For the second time that day, she headed out of town, happily walking on the gravel road again. When she saw a house that looked familiar to her, one with an iron gate in front, bridal wreath by the front porch, and the smell of lilies of the valley in the breeze, she thought it was her grandpa Pitman's house. It looked a lot like it. If so, where was her grandpa's red barn? There was no barn. Her happiness changed to anxiety. She needed to find her family. Where were her siblings, Tom and Mabel? They were fixing the harnesses when she last saw them by the red barn. Her sister Mabel must be riding her horse. She decided to look for Mabel.

As she continued walking on the gravel road, the confusion cleared when she saw Bingo and Perky in the distance. She called for them to come to her, and they did. Together they walked home to her son's farm. She clearly knew where she was now; she was at Russell's farm. Instead of going inside the house, she followed the dogs as they went past the barn and down the hill into the pasture and into the woods. She loved going to the woods. The serenity of it was so refreshing for her. She just drank it in.

The crows above her were noisy. They would stop crowing when they got used to her presence there. The blue jays were scolding her, too. The squirrels didn't care that she was there; they were busy chasing each other up and down the trees. She loved watching the water ripple along the rocks of the creek. It was her favorite spot to be. Today it was a comforting spot for her. She wondered what was happening to her; it was bewildering.

Later that afternoon, as she was still seated in her favorite spot, when she heard the sound of a pickup truck in the distance, she thought it must be her husband Archie. Wasn't it just that morning when she had climbed into the truck with him to go to the pasture? Even though she was in the middle of making her bread, when Archie stood there with that look on his face, one that said, "Why don't you come with me . . . ?" she couldn't refuse him, so she went with him.

While Archie was fixing fence in the pasture of the farm, she sat on the tree stump and thought about how she should be punching down her bread and shaping it into loaves to bake. Why was Archie taking so long today? She heard the sound of a truck again. That must be Archie coming for her.

"Mom, are you all right?" Instead, it was her son getting out of his truck and walking toward her. He had spent a long time looking for her. In fact, his wife and his three children were desperate to find her. It wasn't like her to be gone for such a long time.

Happy at the sight of her son, she got up from the stump and walked with him to the truck and climbed inside; she knew she was finally going home. As the truck made its way up the hill to the farm place, her mind cleared. They drove by the cattle in the feedlot, past the grain bins and into the farmyard. This was Russell's farm; she had lived here since her husband Archie had died ten years ago.

When they pulled in front of the garage, she climbed out of the truck and went inside the house. Russell had remodeled the basement of his rambler house to make an apartment for her, but she generally ate all of her meals with them. For supper that evening, Anne had made scalloped potatoes and ham. No one said anything to her about the episode that day. They had searched a long time for her, they were glad she was safe, but they wondered why she didn't come home.

As she ate her supper, she smiled at the family around her. She was grateful to be living with her son and his family now that her husband was gone. Life was good here. She loved the farm. She enjoyed her grandkids. Her daughter-in-law, Anne, was good to her. She felt safe with them.

Anne got up from the table and went to the kitchen counter to get the cake for dessert. Then Anne passed her a plate with a large piece of chocolate cake with fudge frosting. Her grandson Mark went to the freezer and took out the ice cream. She loved ice cream; vanilla went best with chocolate cake; she hoped it was vanilla. Mark scooped a large scoop of vanilla ice cream and put it on her plate next to her cake. She smiled at him as she slowly enjoyed her dessert.

As Russell ate his cake and ice cream, he looked at his white-haired mother next to him, and he became lost in his thoughts as he reminisced about the days on the Wisconsin farm when her hair was the color of salt and pepper. Whenever he walked into her kitchen after getting off the school bus, he could smell her day. It was chocolate cake, cinnamon rolls, chocolate chip cookies, strawberry jam, or pumpkin pie. On Mondays, the back porch smelled of laundry soap, and her kitchen smelled of spray starch and ironing. She used a wringer style washer, and she pinned the clothes to the clothesline outdoors. He could still hear the sound of the clothes flapping in the wind.

Sometimes their farmhouse lost its usual sense of order, but he didn't mind. Those were the days she was painting the kitchen a bright yellow or wallpapering the living room in soft beige. Sometimes she needed his help, like when she was hanging the new curtains she made for his bedroom or when she was tearing apart the sofa because she was going to upholster it in a brown floral fabric.

She was always busy with something; her duties were many. The jersey cow gave her the milk and cream; she made the butter, the cottage cheese, and the homemade ice cream. Nothing was ever wasted, not even the buttermilk because she used it in her cake recipes. She raised chickens, ducks, geese, and guinea hens. She always had a fresh supply of eggs. Her freezer was full of beef, pork, poultry, frozen fruits, and vegetables. Her garden was often bigger than what she needed so she gave away what she didn't can or freeze. No matter what she was doing, she had time for him when he came home from school. He appreciated that about her.

The dining room table was cleared now, and the dishes were done. Russell could hear her thanking Anne for the wonderful meal. Then she came into the living room to say good night to him. Quietly, she descended the steps to her apartment. She was tired; it had been a long day. She rocked in her rocking chair for a while trying to understand what had happened to her that day.

Why couldn't she find her way home?

She thought about how many times she had taken long trips driving her car to Arizona for the winter, to Wisconsin to visit former neighbors, to Colorado to visit her brother and sister, and to Minnesota to visit her daughter. But today as bewildering as it was, she couldn't find her way home from the pasture by the woods.

To comfort her spirit, she went to her organ and played her favorite hymns, "Jesus Loves Me," "Amazing Grace," and "What A Friend We Have in Jesus." As she played the hymns, she fondly recalled the day she committed her life to Christ, twenty years earlier when she lived on the farm in Wisconsin.

In her kitchen that day, she was mixing a batch of old-fashioned molasses cookies while she was listening to the Radio Bible Class Broadcast. Dr. M. R. DeHaan was giving the plan of salvation, and for the first time in her 50 years, she clearly understood her need to know the Lord in a personal way. At the end of the program, Dr. DeHaan invited anyone who was listening to receive Christ by faith. She remembered how she prayed that day and asked Jesus to forgive her sins and to be her Savior. Then, she found peace of soul, something she hadn't had before that time.

Finally, she grew tired of playing her organ so she found her Bible and she sat in her rocking chair while she read her favorite verses, John 3:16, Ephesians 2:8,9, and Romans 8:28. Gradually, she was feeling better about things. Whatever it was that happened to her that day, she knew that God knew about it, too. She would trust Him to take care of her.

Later, when she crawled into her bed and turned off her bedroom lamp, she did what she always did. She prayed aloud for everyone in her family, for her son, for her daughter, and for her grandchildren. "For Russell, for Anne, for Mike, for Connie, for Mark, for Virginia..." The list continued until she fell asleep.

Upstairs in the living room, Russell and Anne were having serious thoughts about Mom. They were concerned about her, and they had good reason to be. Mom had become rather possessive of her purse by carrying it practically everywhere, and she was always looking for something inside it, but never finding it. For quite a while, Mom had been misplacing her keys, her purse, checkbook, cash, and her important papers. She desperately depended upon Anne to look for them. Once in a while, she put her things in the strangest places. Anne found her purse in the refrigerator and her shoe in the oven. Mom usually covered her embarrassment by laughing and saying, "Now why did I put that there?"

Occasionally, neighbors phoned to say that Mom was with them because they had found her crying as she was walking along the road. Several times, neighbors brought her home when she seemingly forgot the way home. Why was she having these occasional spells of confusion and disorientation? Once she drove her car to Ponca, a town that was familiar to her, and she couldn't find her way home. What was happening to her? Finally, Russell had to disconnect her car battery to keep her from driving to town.

For another safety measure, he took away her hot plate, which she used for simple cooking in her apartment because she forgot to turn it off. Another time, she went outside forgetting that she was running the bath water in the tub. Sometimes she forgot to turn off her TV before going somewhere. All of this forgetfulness was not like her; she was always so careful when she did things.

For a number of years, they had dealt with her depression

and her anxiety. In fact, she could no longer handle living alone on her small farm acreage. Even though it was only a mile away from Russell's farm, it wasn't close enough for her to feel safe. That's why Russell remodeled his basement and made an apartment for her so she could feel safe with them. More and more she had become dependent upon them.

On several occasions, Anne took Mom to Dr. Robinson seeking help for her panic attacks and crying spells. Mom often cried for no obvious reason. If Anne asked why she was crying, Mom could never tell her why. Dr. Robinson always said he could find nothing physically wrong with her. He thought she was suffering from anxiety and depression so he prescribed medication for her. Recently, however, Dr. Robinson also mentioned to Anne that it was possible she was showing early signs of Alzheimer's.

"Russell, remember your mom's last visit to Dr. Robinson?" Anne was talking to her husband in a cautious way. "Remember how I told you that the doctor said she might have early signs of Alzheimer's?"

"Alzheimer's..." Russell sat in his recliner for a long time before he spoke to Anne. He thought about the problems they were having with Mom. Granted, he knew she had slipped now that she was in her seventies, but he also thought about how very "normal" Mom was most of the time. Whenever she was in the pickup with him, whether it was checking cattle, fixing fences or going to town for parts, she was just fine. She quietly enjoyed the ride and didn't do or say anything unusual.

Finally, he turned to Anne and said, "... I doubt it's Alzheimer's. She's seventy-three now. She's just getting forgetful. Sometimes old folks get that way."

Warning Signs on the Prairie
Chapter Three

When you live on the prairie of southern Minnesota, like I do, whether it's daytime or nighttime, you are surrounded by a big sky. Sometimes, the sky is a soft pale blue with not a cloud in sight. Other times, the sky is an incredibly deep blue with wispy clouds here and there. Sometimes it's a bluish green with huge, puffy, white thunderclouds in the distance. Whatever the case, there's always a big sky on the prairie.

When a storm is approaching, there is plenty of warning in the sky as the colors deepen and the clouds roll past. A person can be in denial of the approaching storm by thinking maybe it will miss him, and maybe it will go to the south or to the north of him. A person can choose to be outside working or playing until it gets drastic, until it hails or rains in sheets or until the wind blows strong.

I was in denial for a long time when it came to my mother's condition. I had seen the storm clouds gathering and the warning signs of Alzheimer's that were around her at times, but I didn't want to face it. I stayed in denial. Somehow, ten years managed to pass, and Mom reached the age of eighty-three. My brother and I did the best we could to take care of our mom's needs, and when things got drastic, it demanded our attention.

One evening when Mom was visiting me, the storm clouds that I had been ignoring for so long finally blew me a chilling revelation. That evening my mother didn't know me as her daughter. She was sitting next to me on the sofa in our living room looking at me when she said the words that hurt. "It's been a long time since we had a letter from Virginia. She must be busy with her kids." I felt sick. This was my mother sitting next to me, and she was talking to me as if I were another person. I felt like someone had punched me hard in the stomach.

I wanted to say aloud to her, "Mom, I am your Virginia," but I couldn't get the words out of my mouth because that punch to my stomach left me breathless. I closed the book that I had been reading, and I looked at her tenderly.

Mom was smiling as she continued speaking, " I enjoy Virginia's letters, and I miss hearing from her. Five kids are a handful for her. You know, I only had two children, and that was plenty."

I had made lots of excuses for her failings, but this I could not excuse. Clearly, she didn't recognize me, her only daughter. As I looked at my mother sitting next to me on the sofa, I saw her differently. Instead of my mother and the friend that I had always known, I saw her as a person in need of my care. Our roles in life would dramatically switch; she would be my child, and I would be the mother, her caregiver.

Later that evening, I thought about my mom's aunt Eva and how we used to visit her when I was a little girl. Her house smelled of cats and newspapers, but she could make the best soft sugar cookies that anyone could ever make. I remembered Mother saying that aunt Eva had something called hardening of the arteries, which explained why most of the time aunt Eva lived in the past, and said and did strange things. She lived to be ninety years old, and her two bachelor sons cared for her until she died.

Quite naturally, I concluded that Mom must be like aunt Eva and that she probably had hardening of the arteries. Mom would need my care, and I felt honored. My brother had lovingly taken Mother under his wing after our father died twenty years ago. Now it was my turn, and I was pleased to take that turn. I knew I had to make a home for her with my family so my mom's visit turned into a permanent residency. My husband and my family were supportive, and I was thankful for that. I had no doubts about my ability to take care of my failing mother. After all, if aunt Edna's bachelor sons could do it, so could I.

Mom was still a little homemaker at heart, and I was delighted to have her help. She loved doing dishes. In fact, we often laughed because sometimes we were not finished eating, and Mom was out of her chair busy clearing the table. Her diligence was admirable.

In the days that followed, she became my little shadow. I took her everywhere. It was easy to get along with Mother because of her sweet and quiet nature; she never tried to tell you what to do or how to do it. She wouldn't interfere with your business, and she would go a long way to not bother anyone.

Mom and I were always close. She was the best listener, and she always had time for my brother and for me. No matter what she was doing that day, she stopped and met us in the kitchen to hear about our day at school. She lived her life through ours. Her brown eyes danced, and she smiled as she listened to our stories. She listened and never criticized us; she offered advice only when she felt it was necessary. We were allowed to grow up with a good sense of independence, but always with the utmost respect for her authority.

Mom and I remained friends after I left home, went to college, got married, and had five kids of my own. Over the years, she never lost that part of her that I enjoyed so much, meaning she was still intensely interested in my life. We kept in touch by mail and by phone. She eagerly waited for me to share the details of my life with her, and I did it with great pleasure. When Mom moved from my brother's farm to Colorado to live for four years, I kept in touch by my long detailed letters. Whenever she got one from me, she read it over and over.

Life in Colorado was pleasant for Mom because it was at a senior citizen's pace. She enjoyed being with her sister Mabel, her brother Tom, and her sister-in-law, Lois. Because of her Alzheimer's condition, Mom's mind was often in her youthful days with her family. Mom did well in Colorado because she felt no need to wander and to look for her siblings when she actually was living with them. However, as we know, life has a way of changing. When Mabel died suddenly on Christmas morning, Mom lost her closest companion, which sent her into depression.

Yes, it was best that Mom live with my family and me.

Even though her mind was failing, her body was amazingly healthy. Mom was still an active woman at the age of eighty-three but not as spry as the seventy-three year old who walked to town every day. When she was seventy-seven, she fell and broke her hip. While she was running with Bingo and Perky, the two farm dogs, she tripped over one of them and fell hard in the driveway. It took six hours of surgery to pin her broken hip leaving her with one leg distinctly shorter than the other. She walked with a limp, she wore a shoe with a lift, and she used a walking stick. She didn't give up on her walking; it just took her a little longer.

I was glad that Mom was still an active woman. As a stay-at-home mom, I had a home-based business, a tourist site, gift shop and a bed and breakfast. The childhood home of the classic author, Laura Ingalls Wilder, is near us. As a girl, Laura lived in a sod dugout at Walnut Grove. Later, she wrote about this in her book, *On the Banks of Plum Creek*. When tourists learn that they can stay overnight in a real sod house on the prairie (one that my husband built), dress in prairie clothes, and have breakfast served to them, they give me a call. I am the hostess of the Sod House Bed and Breakfast.

Mom was my little helper for the tourist season in the spring and summer of 1994. She loved being outdoors, and she enjoyed sitting on a bench on our front deck. Whenever someone drove in our driveway, she alerted me by tapping her walking stick on my kitchen window. When it was time to clean for the next guests, Mom helped me put on the new sheets and pillowcases. Together, we cleared the breakfast dishes from the sod house table.

She enjoyed being in a house that was decorated with antiques because she could relate to them. In fact, the spindle chair that sits in our sod house was hers. Whenever she sat in it, she fondly stoked the arms of it and told me that it was her chair. Sadly enough, I knew that much of the time that summer she didn't know me as her daughter. My heart ached inside because she knew her chair, but she didn't know me.

My youngest son was often frustrated because his grandmother called him *Mark* instead of *Tom*. Mom confused Tom with Mark, my brother's youngest son. One day, Tom came into the house to tell me something exciting. As far as he was concerned, his grandma had "won the lottery" because she had finally gotten his name right.

One summer day, Mom made a special point to tell me how much she appreciated the lovely flower garden in the circle of our driveway. "Tell that nice young man who planted the flowers that he did a good job." Mom did not connect that the "nice young man" was my son, her grandson Charlie.

Mom's household cleaning habits changed noticeably. Occasionally, Mom reverted to the old ways of doing things, like the way she cleared the food from our kitchen table. She put the leftover foods, like lunchmeats and cheeses, in the cupboard instead of in the refrigerator without any thought of them spoiling. I couldn't help notice that the way she washed the dishes became strangely unlike her. One day, she didn't use any dishwashing soap. On another day, she had soap in both sides of the sink, lots of soapy water, and she was rinsing the dishes in soapy water. Another time, I found her squirting the hand lotion into the sink thinking it was the soap.

It was obvious that Mom thought I was her sister-in-law because she constantly called me Lois. One day while Mom was doing dishes, I said with a slightly irritated voice, "Mom, I am your Virginia. Please, call me Virginia." And I pointed to myself. At first, Mom acted surprised at my irritated tone, but then she smiled and shrugged her shoulders in a way that told me she knew she was being scolded for something.

By then, she had forgotten what I had said to her, so she excused herself with these words, "Oh well, you can't remember everything." She turned around to the sink and continued washing the dishes. Mom had forgotten who I was and she said, "Oh well, you can't remember everything." Sometimes I laugh at that those words; sometimes I cry at those words.

Whenever neighbors and friends stopped for a visit, Mom usually listened quietly without saying anything. One day, I was surprised when Mom entered into a conversation about raising children as she said, "I had two kids. They weren't any angels. They could raise some Cain in their days." I smiled at the humor of the situation. This was my mother talking about her children. She was telling our neighbor that my brother and I were rascals, but thankfully she didn't give any details. After that, I wondered what she meant by that comment because I always thought we had a reputation for being good kids.

Life settled into a routine after a while, but not without some challenges. Mom didn't like taking a shower, and she hated having her hair washed, which made bath time more difficult. I should have checked into home health care, but I was determined to take care of her myself. In fact, I didn't know about adult daycare services, to give the caregiver a break. Mom always went with me. She stayed in our van, and I did my errands quickly. I especially appreciated the Wal-Mart store near us because it was the only store where I could take her inside and shop for hours. I used their wheelchair that hooked to a shopping cart, and I pushed Mom every-where while I shopped. She enjoyed seeing everything and everyone, especially children.

Since our daughter was away at college, her small upstairs bedroom was a perfect place for Mom because it gave her some privacy. Mom loved being in that little room, but it meant that she had to use our stairway, where the last few steps have a curious little curve to the left with very narrow steps. Mother did fine until the evening she missed a step and fell, leaving her with bruises but no broken bones. Then, I realized she needed to be on the first floor. We didn't have a bedroom on our first floor, but we did have a spacious living room so we rearranged the furniture and made a bedroom for her there.

During the winter months, Mom needed something more to do than dishes and laundry. She didn't want to read the books that I offered her, and she said that letter writing made her nervous. No longer was she interested in sewing or crocheting or making crafts. The programs on television annoyed her because Mom's moral standards were always high; the violence and swearing disgusted her. I bought her some Disney videos to pass the time for her. As the winter dragged on, she needed something more to do than watch videos.

Mom missed having her organ keyboard. She played her favorite hymns for hours whenever she sat down to play it. So my sons drove to Colorado to get her organ and the rest of her personal belongings, which were packed in her little camper trailer. The day my sons carried her organ into the house, she smiled and her eyes twinkled with delight. All of us were happy for her.

We put her organ next to her bed, and she was pleased to have it near her again. Then she sat on the organ bench and lovingly moved her fingers across the keyboard. We waited for her to play a hymn, "Jesus Loves Me," or " Rock of Ages," or "What a Friend We Have in Jesus." When she moved her fingers across the keyboard, a few sour notes played. She sat there for the longest time. Finally, she stood up, turned off the switch, and put away her songbook. We looked at each other with sadness as we realized that Mom had forgotten how to play her organ.

Mom's mind was failing her more and more. But did she know? Did she realize it was happening? I think she did. She struggled with her situation by attempting to cover it as much as she could. Her crying spells were an indication that she knew she was confused, and being confused made her frightened and anxious. In fact, on one occasion, Mom and I talked about it openly. On that afternoon, she told me that she was afraid she was losing her mind. She looked at me with a child-like look that said, "Am I really losing it?" Since I was in denial, I avoided answering her. Instead, I hugged her, and I told her that I would always be there for her. I reminded her that the Lord would be with us. He would not fail us. He would take care of us.

Inwardly, I renewed my personal commitment to her, the same one that I had made over and over in my heart since I was a young girl. I would never put her in a nursing home because I would take care of her all of her days. I loved her as my mother and as my friend. It was my privilege to take care of her no matter how difficult it would get.

That winter her mental confusion was increasing, along with her disorientation to her surroundings. More and more we were becoming strangers to her. She was restless, unpredictable, and at times, rather weird. The disease was taking its toll, but I was more than ever determined to take care of her. There were all kinds of warnings that Mom was suffering from the storms of Alzheimer's, but I wasn't ready to admit it, neither was I ready to seek professional help for her. I stayed in denial.

Instead, I focused my hope on spring, thinking springtime on the prairie would improve everything. Mom loved being outdoors. No doubt, she would be my little helper again. Our place would be busy with the tourists coming to the exhibit and to the gift shop, and the summer would be very busy with guests in our bed and breakfast. Yes, life would be pleasantly busy for both of us; so I thought. I looked forward to spring, but I didn't know that I would be faced with a new set of problems. Eventually, I would close my gift shop. Keeping track of Mom would be more than I could handle. It would be a family effort.

Nothing would be the same for us because Mom was entering the wandering stage of Alzheimer's.

Bright Colors and Ice Cream Sundaes
Chapter Four

Crimson red, sky blue, salmon orange and bright yellow were the colors for Mom's new wardrobe. To make it easier for her to dress herself, we bought pull over tops and pull up slacks with elastic waistbands because buttons and zippers were a problem. We had fun shopping together for her new fashion look. Mom looked great in bright colors because she had beautiful white hair and skin that tanned easily.

The color scheme for her new clothes was part of the plan for keeping track of Mom. Dressing her in bright colors made it easier for us to see her when she felt like wandering. Since Mom loved being outdoors, I wanted her to have some freedom. We live on a twenty-five acre farm site with a house, a barn, a hayshed, a grove of trees, lots of pens for horses, a machine shed, and several buildings in our sod house exhibit. Keeping track of Mom was a challenge.

The landscape is flat on the prairie of southwestern Minnesota where you can see for miles. There are acres and acres of farmland, usually planted to corn and soybeans. From my kitchen window, I can easily see the water tower for the town of Springfield that is eight miles away. If you fly over the prairie, it's like flying over a giant patchwork quilt made of squares because the roadways divide the land into one-mile squares. The precise block that we live on has two miles of paved highways and two miles of gravel roads.

We allowed Mom to walk on the gravel road past our place, but only as far as we could see her bright clothing. We watched her closely to make sure she didn't get to the highway. Most of the time, Mom returned to us when she was out walking, but when she was upset about something, she wandered away from us. If she wandered too far, we had to take swift action by driving our car to get her, only to find that she refused to get into the car. Instead, she stood on the road and tapped her walking stick on the gravel and acted like a stubborn child. No amount of reasoning could change her mind. Finally, we used another tactic that worked like a charm, our Dairy Queen tactic.

What's the chance of having a Dairy Queen on the prairie? One in a million, I would say. Usually, a Dairy Queen is within the city limits of a town with a substantial population. However, one mile to the west of us, we have a Dairy Queen that's out in the middle of nowhere. Why would a Dairy Queen be on the prairie surrounded by farm fields? Amazingly enough, many years ago someone thought it was a good idea to build a Dairy Queen at the intersection of the two longest highways in the nation, east-west highway 14 and north-south highway 71. And it's still there today.

Since Mom loved ice cream, especially butterscotch sundaes, if we invited her to go with us to the Dairy Queen, she climbed into the car. By the time we returned from the Dairy Queen, Mom was content to take her usual place on our deck and finish eating her sundae. I think God put the Dairy Queen there just for us.

Most of the time that summer Mom enjoyed sitting on our deck as a quiet observer of everything going on around her. Sometimes she was content to be inside her camper trailer that was parked by our house. She could be smiling one minute, but in the next minute she could be restless and agitated. Then she went for a walk, but it wasn't really a walk; it was a mission to find someone or some place.

Keeping track of Mom was a family effort. When she wasn't in her usual spot on our deck, we looked in her camper. If she wasn't there, we searched our farm site. Next, we looked up and down our gravel road. If she wasn't there, we became worried. By walking a third of a mile north on the gravel road, she could get to the highway. Because of her mental confusion, if someone stopped to help her, she wasn't able to say our name or give directions to our place. Mom's whereabouts was always a concern for us.

One hot summer day in July, she was missing after our usual search effort had turned up nothing. My panic was real along with my guilt. We had looked everywhere for her. There was a slight chance that she had wandered into a cornfield. How would we find her again? Because the corn was taller than she was, it would take a search party of volunteers to walk the rows of corn, and it would be a nightmare trying to find her. The hot weather would cause her to weaken and dehydrate, and she would perish before we could rescue her. Thankfully, our frantic search was short-lived. It wasn't long before our neighbor Nancy drove into our place. We were instantly relieved to see that Mother was sitting in the back seat, smiling as she was eating her ice cream cone.

Mother had been walking north on our gravel road and was near the highway when Nancy just happened to come along. She stopped and invited her to go for a ride and for a treat at the Dairy Queen. Of course, Mother accepted the invitation. Nancy was not aware of Mom's Alzheimer's condition; she was just being a good neighbor. The amazing thing was the timing of it. We were off our guard, and we let Mom wander too far that day. Nancy came along at just the right time. And how did she know about our Dairy Queen tactic with Mom? She didn't.

Mom's wandering problem was not just a daytime concern; it was also a nighttime concern so we had to safety net our house by locking the doors. Most of the time Mom slept well in her bed in our living room. If she had a restless day and it took longer for me to settle her, I stayed on my brown sofa in our living room until she fell asleep. When she was sound asleep, I quietly went upstairs to my own bedroom.

One Sunday afternoon, I fell into a deep sleep on my brown sofa knowing that Mom was also sleeping on her bed nearby me. When I finally woke up from my long nap, I looked at the bed and expected to see Mom still sleeping in it. Not so. She was gone. Neither was she in the kitchen nor in the bathroom. The front door was unlocked and ajar. I could see she wasn't sitting in her usual spot on the deck, so I scrambled for my shoes, and I ran outside calling for her.

When I walked behind the hayshed, I saw our dog, and I hoped Mom would be close by. Fortunately, she was, and I thanked the Lord for our horses that day. When I found her, she was talking to one of them, a paint mare that we called Beauty. Needless to say after that, I was more careful when I took a nap, and I took time to secure the lock on the kitchen door.

Whenever Mom got extremely restless, I put her in our van, and we went for a ride together hoping to ease her agitation. She was always looking for her family and for the Pitman farm in Illinois. Her mind was living in another place and in another time zone. That's what happens to Alzheimer's people, and that's why they say and do strange things. Mom was living in the days of her youth, perhaps when she was in her twenties or maybe even younger than that, maybe her teens.

On those restless days, as Mom and I drove a couple of miles south to the train tracks, I knew what she was thinking. She was looking for the train depot where she intended to buy a ticket to Lake Villa, Illinois. She just wanted to get home again. Unfortunately, there is no train depot near us, just the train tracks. When we got to the tracks, she usually motioned for me to turn left and follow the road. I'm sure she hoped the road would eventually take her to Lake Villa and specifically to the Pitman farm. Sometimes, we drove around for an hour or so to appease her restless wanderings.

On those restless days, I always tried to keep her in the present time frame by talking about what was happening that day or that week. I tried desperately to keep her from slipping into the past, and it was sad for me to realize she honestly thought that she was going home. Mom would say to me," It's so simple, it's just over that hill. Keep driving. We'll get to the Pitman farm. You'll see." Unfortunately, the Pitman farm was like a mirage for her. As we climbed a hill or made a turn in the road, the Pitman farm sadly disappeared. To compensate for her disappointment, I took her to the Dairy Queen for a butterscotch sundae.

As time went on, her obsession with finding the Pitman farm amplified, and eventually, Mom felt like a prisoner. Because of my refusal to seek professional help for her, I had no way of learning a better way of handling Mom, which was meeting her where she was in her time zone. By pleasantly going along with her, I could have eased her pain. Instead, most of the time I simply ignored the strange things she said to me. Sometimes, I corrected her.

Mom's short-term memory was short, very short. In fact, I made a memory notebook for her. I drew a crude map of Minnesota, and I wrote the words next to it, "You are here." On another page, I drew a map of Illinois and marked where the Pitman farm was at Lake Villa. On another page, I drew a map of Nebraska showing where Russell's farm was located. On another page, I drew a map of Colorado showing where she had lived for four years. I often used the memory map book to remind her of the geographical facts. I hoped it would keep her confusion from deepening.

Telling Mom the truth was a very important thing for me, and I struggled with that issue. I could not lie to Mom, I had never lied to her, and I wasn't about to do it then. I was staunch about the truth, too staunch. When she asked me where Mabel was, I told her the truth by saying, "Mom, your sister died a year and a half ago. You were there when it happened. You remember, don't you?" Of course, Mom's response was to cry for the loss of her sister, and then I felt bad when I saw her crying. After that, I avoided giving her an answer when she asked me painful things. Yet, I could have learned a better way to handle that situation. And in time, I did learn a better way.

I was in denial. Why was I in denial? I guess it was my

way of protecting myself from the pain because I was trying to hold on to the Mother that I once knew. Seemingly, if I were to let her go, I would have to admit that I was losing her. She was suffering from a disease that I refused to acknowledge. To acknowledge it, I would have to walk through a door that I didn't want to walk through. I would have to open a Pandora's box and look inside. I didn't want to go there.

I never fully considered the awful dilemma Mom faced. At times she must have wondered who we really were. She must have thought, "Who are these people? These folks look so familiar to me, but I just can't place them." To cover her embarrassment of not knowing us, she compensated by smiling warmly at us. She always said, "There you are." That was a great cover-up for not knowing exactly who the "you" was.

Since Mom never wanted to be a burden for anyone, nor did she ever wish to wear out her welcome, it was understandable that she wanted to leave, to go home to her family. After all, as far as she was concerned, she had been gone far too long. Her family must be worried by now. Although she appreciated the kindness of the people she was with, she knew she needed to get back to Illinois. What a predicament it was for her! No wonder she was agitated, and no wonder she wandered.

Some of her crying spells were probably caused by her thinking about her family, "My family doesn't know where I am. They must be worried about me. I never told them good-bye." Seemingly to them, she had just disappeared one day. Time seemed so endless for her; her situation seemed hopeless; the frustration escalated for her. Mom's way of dealing with the pain and frustration was to cry, and we could not console her. Nothing we said would help. Nothing we did would help.

One night, I had a dream that momentarily put me in my mother's shoes. I was a little girl again, and I found myself walking the streets of Silver Lake, Wisconsin, a small town that was familiar to me in my childhood. I didn't know where I was going, and I wondered why I was there. I walked and walked. Nothing made sense to me. I wished someone could tell me what I was doing there. When I saw a lot of people at the beach by the lake, I eagerly searched the crowd. I looked for my mom, I looked for my dad, and I looked for faces that were familiar to me. I found none.

Naturally, I wanted to go home to our farm, but I was too young to drive, and if I started walking there, I wasn't certain I could find the right way. I needed help from someone familiar, perhaps a neighbor or a friend. I walked and walked the streets trying to find just one familiar person. I wanted to scream, "I'm lost . . . help me." But instead, I said nothing, and I silently moved from person to person. Then I saw a figure in the distance that looked like my father. Oh, there's my dad! He's coming for me. "Dad?" But the man kept walking, he didn't know me, and I was left alone on the sidewalk. It was the loneliest feeling in the world. Finally, I woke up.

Thankfully, it was just a dream, and I woke up to reality. Alzheimer's people are not dreaming; they can't wake up from the confusion. It's a nightmare for them. So, they usually say and do strange things. Understandably, it is very important for the family to take time to analyze them by asking some basic questions. What time are they living in? What are they trying to do? Where are they trying to go? And why? Then play along with them. Meet them where they are, but always on pleasant terms.

In the spring of 1995, Mom was desperately trying to find the Pitman farm in Illinois. In spite of all of my efforts, Mom's wandering had increased, and I knew that I had to do something. I decided to take Mom to Lake Villa so we could visit her roots and find the Pitman farm, if there were such a farm. Maybe then, she would be satisfied. If she walked the streets of Lake Villa again, she would see that everything had changed since she was a little girl. She would know that her father and her mother, her grandmother and her grandfather were not living anymore. Then she would realize that the past was gone, and she needed to live in the present. This would end her restless wanderings. We would return to Minnesota, and she would be content to stay with me. No more wanderings; just happy days for us.

I was so wrong. I did not understand this thing called Alzheimer's.

Hallucinations of Aunt Alice
Chapter Five

When I was a young girl, my mom's aunt Alice lived with us for a while on our farm in Wisconsin. Even now it's easy for me to visualize her. She was an austere woman in her eighties, alert, spry, and slender. Her extremely long white hair was always tied in a knot on the top of her head, and she wore wire-framed glasses. She was very straight-laced and very English. Since she never wore slacks, she wore dresses made from checked gingham, usually blue or green, and like most farmwomen of that era, she always wore an apron over her dress.

I remember a time when Mom and I looked for a drug store that sold Fitch shampoo, aunt Alice's favorite kind. As we were shopping, Mom told me she felt that aunt Alice was a little peculiar because when she washed her hair, which was only once a month, she used the whole bottle of Fitch shampoo, all at once.

Aunt Alice was a great helper for Mom. She washed dishes, and she helped Mom with the cooking and baking. She worked in the garden, and she helped with the canning and freezing of the fruits and vegetables. On washdays, she hung clothes on the line, and she helped with the ironing and mending.

I never heard the reason why aunt Alice had never married. Perhaps she didn't want to get married. She worked and lived in Chicago most of her lifetime. Needless to say, aunt Alice was strangely unpredictable. One autumn day when we got off the school bus, we were surprised to find that Aunt Alice had moved out, and she had gone back to Chicago without saying good-bye to my brother and me. Later that winter, our family was notified that Aunt Alice died alone in her apartment on Christmas Eve.

Almost forty years later, Aunt Alice came back to haunt me; that is in a sense, because Mom was having hallucinations of her. It was rather disheartening for me to have Aunt Alice interfere with my plans. After all, I had planned our trip to keep Mom in the present moment and to discourage her living in the past. I hoped the trip would help Mom think more clearly, but instead she was getting worse.

Our trip started on a high point as we returned to my roots in southeastern Wisconsin, to the farm that I had left when I was eighteen. When I was a senior in high school, my parents moved from the farm to live in Sioux City, Iowa. Over the years the farm had changed greatly, so it was a rather bittersweet time for me when we pulled into our old driveway. After all, not only had the farm changed, but we also had changed. By then, I was a married woman with five children, and my mom had been a widow for nearly twenty years.

Mom and I sat in our car wistfully looking at our old farmhouse. I wished we could step inside it once again. I was feeling rather bold that day, bold enough to make my wish come true. I got out of the car, walked up to the house, climbed the steps, and knocked on the door hoping that someone would answer my knock. Suddenly, the door opened, and I stood face to face with a white-haired lady who quite naturally invited me inside her house. I gestured to my mom who was still sitting in the car. Together we stepped inside the kitchen of my youth. Our gracious host made us a cup of tea and offered us some cookies. Choking back tears, my eyes slowly surveyed the humble kitchen and the adjoining living room. I knew that I would review that scene over and over in my mind, long after we had left it.

Next, we went to Lake Villa, Illinois, where Mom was born and raised. It's not a very big town, so we drove around the business district and the housing district several times while Mom beamed with excitement. She was pleasantly connecting with her roots. She didn't say much to me, but her smile indicated she was having nice thoughts. I was happy for her.

Later, we had lunch together in a small café. Then, we drove to the lake, sat in the park for a while, and watched the water as it playfully hit the rocks along the beach. As I sat there, I tried to imagine mom's parents as living people, with real faces and personalities. I never had the chance to know them because both had died before I was born. I only knew their names, Jesse Mae Pitman and Thomas Brompton, and their images from the old photos.

Thomas Brompton emigrated from Collingham, England to the United States, with his parents when he was thirteen years old. Eventually, he owned and operated a meat market at Lake Villa. He married Jesse Pitman, and together they had four children. One daughter died at twenty-two months from spinal meningitis. Sadly enough, his wife Jesse died rather suddenly after a gall bladder surgery in 1924 when she was forty-nine. Mom was fourteen when it happened.

Mom's father later bought the Pitman farm, and he was living there when he died in 1942 at the age of sixty-seven. Eventually, the Pitman farm was sub-divided for housing. After my parents were married, my father actually built their home in the housing section that at one time was the Pitman farm. I lived in that home until I started school. That's when my parents moved to the Wisconsin farm.

Amazingly, on our visit to Lake Villa, Mom and I actually found the Pitman farm. There were no living relatives in the area to connect with and to ask for directions to the farm, so we had to look for it ourselves. Mom insisted that it was on a road called Petite Lake Road. We found that road just north of Lake Villa. As we were driving along, suddenly Mom said with confidence, "Oh, there's the Pitman farm!"

I wasn't that certain. We drove into the driveway and looked around, but no one was home that day to confirm whether it was or wasn't the Pitman farm from Mom's past. I took several pictures of the farmhouse and the red barn. When we returned home from our trip, I compared the photos to old pictures from Mom's family album. Mom was right;

it was the Pitman farm.

Later that afternoon, we drove to the Lake Villa Cemetery where her father, her mother, and her infant sister were buried. I remember visiting it as a little girl and placing flowers on their graves so I had no trouble finding the cemetery, but finding their graves was not as easy. I sat in our car wondering which direction to start looking. Mom, however, got out of our car and spontaneously walked to the graves just like she did when I was a little girl.

At the cemetery, I took pictures of the headstones, close-ups so that we could read the words and the dates. I had Mom stand by the headstones. When Mom slipped into the past, the photos would keep her in the present by reminding her of the day we visited her family's graves. My aim was to keep Mother in the present moment.

Mom and I were having the best time together because she was acting "normal." We stayed with former neighbors and friends for all of the nights on our trip, that is, until the last night of our trip when we checked into a motel in Iowa. That's when Mom's condition turned bizarre. Mom said that aunt Alice was in the room with us. How could she? Aunt Alice was dead. Didn't Mom remember that she had died?

Aunt Alice, with her long white hair tied in a knot on top of her head and with her wire-framed glasses, was strangely revisiting us that night. Mom was having hallucinations, comfortable visions of Aunt Alice, and I was terrified with it. I kept thinking this couldn't be happening. Our trip to the Pitman farm and to the cemetery was supposed to help clear her mental confusion, now Mom was seeing aunt Alice. Things were getting gravely worse.

Not only was Mother having hallucinations, but she also was restless and agitated. She refused to go to bed that evening because she was paranoid that someone was breaking into our motel room and stealing our things, and she insisted that I call the police. Mom was out of control. I had never seen her like that, and it frightened me that I could not calm her. The restlessness continued far into the night. The next morning as we were checking out of the motel, Mom said, "Where's aunt Alice? She's going with us!"

As we traveled to Minnesota that day, Mom kept scolding me for leaving aunt Alice at the motel. No amount of talking and reasoning could change her mind. As I drove along, I had a little chat with myself. It was time that I faced the seriousness of Mom's condition. Mom had become unmanageable. I needed to get professional help for her. I promised myself that I would do that. At home again, Mom settled down for me, and she was nearly normal, except for a slight mention that aunt Alice was staying in her former bedroom upstairs. Sadly enough, Mom had no memory of taking the trip.

As I had promised myself, I made an appointment for Mom with our family physician, Dr. Schmitz. He asked me to give him a written report of her behavior before our visit with him. I wrote about her short-term memory loss, her inability to recognize her family, her mood changes, her crying spells, her anxiety, her frustration, her restlessness, her wandering, and the weird and bizarre time with aunt Alice.

Dr. Schmitz told me what I had feared and denied all along: Mom fit the profile for Alzheimer's. There was no medical test that he could do to absolutely confirm it, short of an autopsy. Considering all of the things that I had written about Mom, it was fairly clear to him that she had Alzheimer's disease. Now that our doctor had spoken the word, Alzheimer's, I actually felt a sense of relief. I could look to him for some professional help. He prescribed medication for her anxiety and restlessness and gently suggested that I consider a nursing home.

When Dr. Schmitz wrote on Mom's chart, Alzheimer's/ Dementia, I had to face the situation with no more looking away, no more excuses and no more denial. Loving someone can cover a multitude of failings, but it could no longer cover the reality of Alzheimer's disease. He gently patted Mom's shoulder as he escorted her to the waiting room and told me to stay in his office because he would be back to talk to me.

"Your mother is extremely healthy; she could live a long time yet. The fact is Alzheimer's is slowly affecting her brain. Someday, when she is seated at the table, she will forget how to pick up her fork and feed herself," he said. It was hard for me to imagine my little, ice cream-loving mother not being able to feed herself. Dr. Schmitz looked serious as he continued speaking to me, "She will need long-term care."

When I returned to the waiting room, Mom was smiling at the toddler who was knocking the magazines off the coffee table and on to the floor. As I reached down to pick them up again, I noticed one of the magazines was featuring an article about Alzheimer's disease, so I skimmed the article. It explained that over four million people in the United States suffer with Alzheimer's. Approximately, 35% of those over eighty-five years old have the disease. A pang of sorrow hit me; my mom was now a statistic.

As we were driving home that day, I thought about Dr. Schmitz's suggestion that I consider a nursing home for Mom. Unfortunately, my impression of a nursing home was not a good one. I was determined to keep her at home. I saw Mom as a little bird that was used to being free, and I couldn't put her in a cage. She loved her walks, and she loved being outdoors in the summer. How could I put her in a place where she couldn't be outside when she wanted to be? I also saw Mom as a delicate flower that would wither and droop if she didn't have the sunshine she needed to survive. I pictured her in her nursing home room all shriveled and forlorn. No, I just couldn't do that to her. Somehow, we would find a way to keep Mom.

That evening as I was putting Mom to bed, I remembered the magazine article on Alzheimer's, the one I saw in the doctor's office. My mom was now a statistic; she was one of four million people with Alzheimer's disease. There was no comfort in cold, hard statistics, but I knew where I could find my comfort. I sank in my favorite brown sofa, and I opened my

Bible to a familiar verse, Romans 8:28, KJV, "And we know that all things work together for good to them that love God, to them who are the called according to his purpose."

For the first time on the journey, I surrendered whole-heartedly to the idea that my mother had Alzheimer's. She had been showing us warning signs all along the way for nearly fifteen years, but somehow I had managed to stay in denial. I was the closest person to her, yet I was the last person to acknowledge it.

That afternoon at the office, Dr. Schmitz explained that Alzheimer's people have plateaus. They are stable for a while, they fall deeper, and they are stable again. He handed me a booklet about the stages of Alzheimer's disease. It was depressing when I read it. That evening, I needed spiritual comfort. My heart was very troubled about the future that I was facing. Again I looked at Romans 8:28, one of Mom's favorite verses. It was the Lord's promise that all things would work together for our good. I imagined Mom's voice confidently reminding me to trust in the Lord.

Then I got up from the sofa, and I made myself a cup of tea. When I came back to my Bible, which was still open to the eighth chapter of Romans, I continued reading. When I got to verse thirty-eight, I found some powerful words of comfort, "For I am convinced that neither death nor life, neither angels nor demons, neither the present nor the future, nor any powers, neither height nor depth, nor anything else in all creation will be able to separate us from the love of God that is in Christ Jesus our Lord."

I grabbed my pen, and I slowly and confidently wrote in the margin of my Bible these words, "Not even Alzheimer's will be able to separate us from the love of God."

Not even Alzheimer's.

My Clothesline Decision
Chapter Six

Outwardly, that summer I appeared at ease with those around me, and I seemed to be enjoying my everyday business routine with the visitors to our tourist exhibit. Inwardly, I was a wreck because I was struggling with what to do with Mom. In March, Dr. Schmitz had recommended a nursing home, but I wanted to keep her at home, yet it was getting more difficult to care for her at home.

I struggled with guilt because there were so many things that I missed because of my commitment to Mom. My husband and I spent very little time together, and we were drifting. My children were growing up without me, as I couldn't be there for them when they were doing the things that teenagers do in high school and in college. I felt so helpless and so guilty. Someone once described this problem as the sandwich time of life. Your children have needs, your parents have needs, and you feel like you and your husband are in the middle of the sandwich. Squeezed!

That summer was a constant whirlwind of activity for me as my workload increased. Her crying spells, agitation, mood swings, hallucinations, and restless wanderings had worsened even though she was on medication. She needed more and more of my time and my care. I was exhausted, partly from my work and partly from my emotional turmoil. I knew Mom needed nursing home care, but I couldn't change my promise to her, so I just kept going until I reached a breaking point. I was hanging sheets on our clothesline on the last Friday of July when it came.

A TV crew from Sioux Falls was scheduled to be at our place at noon that day to interview me and film the sod houses. They were doing a feature called "Trip on a Tank Full." Our sod house exhibit was the perfect distance from Sioux Falls for tourists to drive to us and return on a tank full of gas. The television exposure would be great advertisement for my business, but my enthusiasm was dulled by my concern for Mom's future.

My bed and breakfast guests were leaving, and my new guests would be arriving by late afternoon. I needed to clean the sod house, put on the new bedding, and do my dirty dishes. Mom was not the little helper that she was the previous summer because she refused to walk out to the sod house every time that I needed to be there. Instead, she looked for a way to escape.

In our back yard, I was hanging bed sheets on the clothesline. In a rare moment of privacy for me, I let the tears come. My soul was agitated with indecision because I was still hanging on to Mom. I grabbed a clothespin from the basket and pinned one corner of the sheet to the line. I stretched the sheet as far as it would go, and with another pin I fastened the other corner to the clothesline. I was stretched. Just like the sheets on the line, I was stretched. Finally, I broke with these words "I can't do this anymore. Lord, help me to do the right thing."

At the clothesline that day, I decided to put Mom in a nursing home. I had wrestled with that decision for five months since March when Dr. Schmitz had gently suggested the idea to me. Mom was failing, and she needed more care than I could give her. I was physically and mentally exhausted. It was my breaking point.

Would God honor such a decision? I was going to break my promise to her, the one I made to her when I was a little girl. I always said I would never put Mom in a nursing home. I loved her; we were bonded. I thought that love was all I needed to keep me going. It took lots of love and patience to care for her twenty-four hours a day.

Mother wasn't my smiling butterscotch Mom of last summer. I tried everything to make her happy again, but I couldn't do it. She cried so much of the time, and she was restless and agitated. In fact, she was my little prisoner; her brightly colored clothes were her prison clothes.

In my agony at the clothesline, I soon became aware of God's comforting presence with me, assuring me that He knew my struggle. Since it was a Friday morning when I made the decision, I knew I couldn't act upon it until Monday. I asked my husband and my children to keep me from changing my mind over the weekend because my heart had so much anguish.

On Monday, I phoned Dr. Schmitz. "It's time for me to do something different with Mom," I said, "What do I do?"

"Just make a phone call to the nursing home that you want for your mother, and they will help you," he said.

My choice was St. John Lutheran Home in Springfield, a beautiful facility with an awesome reputation. It was near to me, only eight miles away. My next phone call to St. John Home produced quick results. "We have a room for your mother right now. Bring her to us at 10:30 on this Friday. Make an appointment with her doctor for a physical on Wednesday. See you on Friday."

God honored my clothesline decision with amazing timing. One phone call had placed her in the facility of my first choice. I was hoping to place Mom somewhere by fall or early winter. I knew that St. John Lutheran Home had a waiting list, so I was startled when the social worker said to me; "We have a room for your mother right now . . ."

As the nursing home requested, we scheduled an appointment for a physical with Dr. Schmitz on Wednesday. He said," You just called me on Monday, and you're going on Friday. Some people wait for a long time before they have an opening. That's amazing."

Dr. Schmitz assured me that I was doing the right thing for Mom, especially because he recognized changes in her since March. He reminded me that Alzheimer's people have plateaus where they stay the same for a period of time, and then they drop to a lower level where they stay for a while.

Every person's timetable is different. He reminded me that Mother was extremely healthy, and she could live many years yet. The longer she lived; the more care she needed. I was doing the right thing.

As we drove home from the doctor's appointment, I thought about Mom's changing condition. She needed help going to the bathroom; sometimes there were accidents. She dressed herself every day, but I had to put out new clothes each evening for her to wear the next day. If I didn't do that, she wore unmatched outfits, or she wore the dirty clothes from the day before.

In spite of the medication she was taking, she had crying spells daily, and there was nothing that I could do to comfort her; I felt so helpless. In fact, I could no longer leave her with my children because of her mental confusion and her hallucinations. If I did leave her for just a brief time, when I returned home, she told me wild stories of what my children did when I was gone, so I couldn't leave her with them anymore. It was too upsetting for everyone.

Mom constantly asked me about her sister Mabel because she wanted to know where she was and why she hadn't been able to play card games with her any more. Mabel had died on Christmas morning three years before that. Mom was there when it happened, but she had no memory of it.

One evening at dusk, Mom was looking out of our kitchen window to the plowed field across our gravel road. Then she went to the closet, took out her coat, put it on, and grabbed her walking stick. She was heading out the kitchen door when my son Steve stopped her. "Grandma, you can't go out now! It's too cold. It's getting dark." That evening, Mom took on a different personality when she became angry because Steve blocked her way at the door. She not only hit him with her walking stick, but she also swore at him as she tried to get out the door because she had seen her sister Mabel riding her pony across the plowed field, and she needed to go to her before she rode too far away.

My gentle Christian mother was swearing in her anger and using her walking stick to hit someone who got in her way. Mom would have been ashamed of herself with such behavior. Later, I learned that it was a condition called sun downing. Alzheimer's people are more disorientated and confused at the time of sun down, and sometimes they turn violent when someone interferes with what they want to do. We waited for her mood to change. I gently put my arms around her and guided her to our living room. The sight of her organ next to her bed calmed her spirits. She never played it, but it was her security in a world that was strangely darkening all around her.

One day, she wandered through the cattle pens to the north pasture, and we found her in the northeast corner of the pen looking like a cornered animal. The barbed wire fence stopped her, and she was crying. My heart ached at the sight of her trapped in the corner. Slowly, we gently guided her back to the house. Mom was no longer my smiling companion; she was my prisoner.

Mom's obsession with finding the Pitman farm worsened. Sometimes she woke up in the night, dressed herself, and tried to go outside to hunt for the Pitman farm. We never knew what she would do next. During the day, she tried to make her escape when we weren't watching her closely.

One day just as my B & B guests were arriving, Mom was heading south on our gravel road trying to escape from us. I was embarrassed, as I had to explain the situation to my guests, Crosby and Barb of St. Paul. They quickly understood what was happening, and Crosby graciously offered to go after her. Amazingly, she trusted him enough to get inside his car so he could bring her home.

On another day, Mom came inside the house with a bouquet of flowers that she had picked from our flower garden. I thought she had picked them for me, but I saw tears in her eyes. She said, "Grandma's real sick today. Let's go see her now. I picked these flowers for her." She was like a little child, so sincere, yet so sadly confused.

Mom was always waiting for her father to come for her, and she constantly asked me to phone her father. After I read the booklets that Dr. Schmitz gave me, I learned how to play along with her idea of calling her dad. Before that time, I was always trying to keep her in the present moment. So, I would say to her, "Mom, how old are you? You're eighty-five years old now. Could your dad still be living? Of course not, he's been gone for a long time. Don't you remember that? He died before I was born." Anguish came to her face as she sat in a chair and cried "Dad's gone. Dad's gone. Dad's gone."

Eventually, I learned to say to her, "Of course, we can call your dad, but I think he's busy with a customer in his meat market right now. Could you finish folding these bath towels for me? Then, we will call him later." By the time the last towel in the basket was folded, she was content again.

Every night at bedtime, she looked at me as if to say, "Where do I sleep?" It was as if she had arrived at our house for the first time. Every night, I had to escort Mom to her bedroom in our living room. Then we walked to our bathroom, and I helped her with her personal needs. I helped her wash herself, undress, and put on her flannel nightgown. Then we set out new clothes on her chair next to her bed. I gently helped her into her bed, and I tenderly tucked her into the sheets, like she used to do with me when I was a child. For many nights that summer, I slept on the sofa in the living room to be near her.

Yes, Mother's condition had deteriorated in the last few months. I had good reason to be placing her in a nursing home where she could get the care she needed right now and in the future. But, my heart ached for her. That evening as I helped her undress for bedtime, I was sad. She was so unsuspecting of what was going to happen to her tomorrow. I was glad to be spared the task of explaining to her why I had made the clothesline decision. She was like a child now; no explanation was necessary.

When Mom was finally tucked into her bed, I sat on my

brown sofa in the living room because I knew I wouldn't get much sleep that night. Tomorrow would be the hardest day of my life, and I dreaded it. For a long time, I tenderly observed my mom lying in her bed. She often made strange sounds, strange whispers. That evening I decided to tune into what she was saying as she whispered, so I crawled my way across the living room floor to her bedside using a slow crawl because I did not want to disturb her. Then, I listened to what she was saying as she whispered.

"For Russell . . . for Virginia . . . for Anne . . . ." The list went on and on. My mom was praying, and I was humbled by it. Surprisingly, she was alert enough to pray for us by our names, the names that I thought she had forgotten. Hearing my mother speak my name aloud, somehow took me back to the time when Mom was free of Alzheimer's. For a long time, I sat next to her bed, and I pondered everything. That evening, Mom knew who I was; she knew that I was her daughter, Virginia. Amazingly, she was praying for me. What did this mean? Was I doing the right thing for her tomorrow? I was having second thoughts about it. I was weakening.

I was questioning my clothesline decision.

A Special Home For Mom
Chapter Seven

That night on my brown sofa, I dozed off and on thinking about my clothesline decision. My mind and my heart agonized over Mom. If she was capable of being alert enough to whisper my name in prayer, perhaps there was hope for her to get better. Perhaps, I should hold on to her by keeping her at home longer. I prayed and asked God for wisdom because I wanted to do the right thing. At sunrise I had peace about what I was going to do that day. Sometime in the night, I turned on the lamp beside me, and I grabbed my Bible for comfort. I read John 14: 1-2, a very comforting passage. While I read the passage, certain phrases jumped at me, as if God were answering my cry for help. "Don't let your hearts be troubled . . . trust in God . . . I am going there to prepare a place for you . . ."

Even though my heart was aching, those amazing words told me not to be troubled about things because God was going ahead of us to prepare a place for us. Without being there yet, I knew St. John Lutheran Home was going to be a special home for Mom. I decided to stay firm with my clothesline decision, and my soul was at peace because I knew I was doing the right thing. The timing of things also gave me assurance that God was in the decision. My first phone call to the nursing home brought surprisingly fast results, "We have a room for your mother right now . . . Bring her to us at 10:30 on Friday."

Early the next morning, I packed Mom's things in the same blue suitcase that she brought with her from Colorado when she came to visit me two years before that. As I put her things in the suitcase, I had a sick queasy feeling in my stomach because I was worried about how Mom would behave.

Would she cry? Would she insist on coming home with me? Would she cling to me like a child? I had no way of knowing what she would do, so I had to trust that God would take care of everything. For some moral support that day, I asked my twelve-year-old son, Tom, to come with us.

As we drove down the long lane to St. John Lutheran Home, I saw the beauty and the style of the place that was soon going to be my mom's new home. The two-story brick building with stained glass windows had a large canopy for an entrance. On the north side of the building was a beautiful courtyard with a huge water fountain. I parked our van in the spacious parking lot, and we walked up the sidewalk to the front entrance. Two sets of automatic doors sensed our presence, and we walked inside. Mom followed me just like a puppy follows its master. She trusted me completely.

A salesman with a briefcase was standing by the front desk. I heard him make this comment to the receptionist. "Wow, this is a great place. It belongs in Minneapolis. You're here on the prairie, and you have this!" Then Mary Lynn, the social worker, stepped out of her office and welcomed us with a smile. Mom and Tom sat in the lounge while I followed Mary Lynn into her office where I filled out some paper work.

Then we met with a nurse named Wendy who issued Mom a security bracelet that would set off an alarm if she approached certain doors that led outdoors. At that time St. John did not have an Alzheimer's unit, so Mom was being placed in a regular room with a roommate on a nurse's station that was called "three south."

Then Wendy walked with us to the second floor where she introduced us to the staff. Later the charge nurse Mary took us to room 223 to meet Helma, Mom's roommate. Helma spontaneously took Mom's hand in hers and said, "I'm never alone. I have Jesus with me all of the time." She pointed to her picture of Jesus on the wall above her bed. Then Helma went to her organ, sat on the bench, and played "Jesus Loves Me," and Mom smiled at hearing one of her favorite songs. With that, I was feeling much better about things.

As we unpacked Mom's blue suitcase, we hung a few of her clothes in the closet, and we put the rest of her things in her dresser and her nightstand. When I asked nurse Mary if we could have Mom's organ in her room for her, she said she would gladly make room for it. "It's always nice for our residents to have a familiar piece of furniture. It makes them feel more like home," she said.

Mom's room was decorated in mauve and green wallpaper, giving it a feeling of being at home. The balloon valance over the window matched the wallpaper border that wrapped its way around the room. The twin bedspreads were color-coordinated to the wallpaper and valance. The chairs were also color-coordinated to the room. They were of a matching printed cloth, but they had a thick, plastic, protective coating that made them shine.

Mom soon got restless so we took a walk together. First, we walked past the day room where my son Tom was in a lounge chair watching the big screen TV, then past the small dining area in front of the nurse's station. Then we walked to the end of a hallway where we discovered a bird aviary. Mom, of course, enjoyed seeing and hearing the tiny birds as they flew, ate, and nested in the indoor cage made especially for them.

As we walked along, I noticed only clean smells, not the sterile antiseptic clean of a hospital, but the fresh clean smell of a home. When I saw Fran, the cleaning lady, I stopped and complimented her on doing an excellent job. I teased her that she could come to my house any day to clean for me. Fran just laughed, smiled, and said, "I get that invitation all the time."

As we made our way back to Mom's room, I noticed that the rooms were decorated with various colors. The floral wallpaper made each room resemble a bedroom in someone's home. As we walked along, I stopped to admire the elegant wall hangings in the hallways, and the many beautifully framed pictures that decorated the space between the rooms.

Finally, we ended our walk by stopping at the nurse's

station. I indicated to Mary that it was time for me to go home. I dreaded to think what Mom would do just then. For two years, Mom had been my constant companion. How would she take it when I had to leave her? Nurse Mary sensed my concern, and she assured me that Mom would do just fine without me.

I gave Mom a hug and turned to walk away. Then Tom and I walked down the hallway to the elevator that would take us to the first floor and to the front desk. We did this without looking back. I couldn't bear seeing the look on Mom's face just then, as she stood with Mary. From that time on, I made it my policy to not look back. Whenever it was time for me to leave her side, I always gave her a hug, I told her I loved her, and I turned away from her without looking back.

Before leaving the building that day, I stopped to see Mary Lynn again. I told her it was hard for me to leave Mom. We chatted about other things, and then I indicated that I needed to go home because Tom was waiting for me outside in the parking lot. "I'll sit with your mom now. I can sit with her for a while to keep her company to help her feel at home here." Imagine that? The Director of Social Services was offering to sit with my mom to make her feel more at home. Then Mary Lynn got up from her desk and headed the direction of Mom's room, looking back at me with a smile. Now I had peace of mind. Tom and I could finally go home.

The next day, I found myself in an emotional low because I had negative thoughts about what I had done with Mom. I knew that Mom had trusted me completely because she followed me inside the nursing home like a puppy follows it master. I felt like I had betrayed her trust. Would she give me that "traitor" look? What would she do when she realized I had placed her in a nursing home? Somehow, I felt like I had let her down. I cried every time I thought of Mom because I missed her. Yet, I knew that God had honored my decision because the day had gone smoothly for us, better than I had anticipated. St. John Lutheran Home was a beautifully decorated new home for

Mom, a special place to be when you need that type of care.

Because I cried easily that day, I stayed home and went to visit her the next day. I knew my tears would upset Mom; she could read my emotions like she could read a book. We were close, and we understood each other so well. I always tried to be upbeat around her. Fortunately, the staff knew how to gently orient Mom to her surroundings. So I really didn't need to worry about Mom adjusting to it. Rather, I was the one facing the strangeness of Mom's new home. Like any new situation in life, it took time for me to get used to visiting Mom in her new home.

Initially, I had a problem with seeing the other residents that lived on Mom's floor. So many of them sat expressionless in wheelchairs and in geriatric chairs. I wondered what Mom would think when she looked around at these other residents. Would it upset her? So for the first few days, I observed her closely to see how she was reacting to what she saw around her. I found that she had no reaction to those around her; she appeared to be in her own little world adapting well to her new home. I was the one who needed time to adjust to it all.

Whenever I visited Mom, I must admit that I was never able to avoid a certain feeling that I had each time I stepped into the elevator on first floor. After pushing the button for second floor, I stood waiting for the door to open again, and I always had a queasy feeling inside me. You see, when it's your mom, you deeply feel the hurt, and that queasy feeling never went away for me. In fact, it got worse as her condition worsened.

Here's how I learned to deal with the sick feeling inside me. When the elevator door opened again, and I stepped out on second floor, I usually took a deep breath; and I deliberately made myself think positively about Mom's situation. (She was safe. She lived in a lovely home. She was treated with respect. She had trained staff taking care of her. She had adapted well to her new home, and etc.) As I headed down the hallway past rooms 200, 202, 204, 206, 208, and 210, I had enough time to lessen that queasy pain inside of me.

A house is a house, but a home is a home. Eventually, St. John Lutheran Home became home for Mom and for me. People make a home, and St. John Lutheran Home had lots of people. Residents, nurses, nurse aides, high school aides, laundry personnel, cleaning ladies, custodians, a receptionist at the front desk, cooks, kitchen crews, department for activities, dietician, bookkeepers, an administrator, a pastor and a chaplain. As time went on, I came to know them as individuals; I got an intimate view of their routine. The best part is I found them to be real people. A house is a house, but a home is a home. Maybe that's why they call it St. John Lutheran Home.

And then, there's Parker, a red Irish setter that lives at St. John Lutheran Home. Whenever he feels like going outside, he walks up to the automatic doors of the front entrance and waits for them to open for him. He casually walks outside as the doors close behind him. He takes his walk, does his business, and comes back inside. Even though Parker is well fed by the staff, he roams around the facility hoping for a treat or two. He has his regular rounds to do, going from room to room checking the wastebaskets for possible food items.

When Mom lived with us, she enjoyed our dog, our black Lab named Katie. She used to bend down to Katie, pat her on the head, and tell her what a good dog she was. Mom also enjoyed Parker. She smiled at him when he came into her room, sniffed at her wastebasket and then went on his way to another room. Parker had a natural way of making Mom feel at home.

As I observed the nurses and the nurse aides in action, I soon recognized that it was not just a job for them, but it was also a ministry. They made the residents feel like they were in a place where self-respect prevailed. They never talked down to them, nor did they treat them as children. They treated them as adults and with dignity. They always called the residents by their first names. They made eye contact with them, even if it meant squatting to a wheelchair level. They spoke in friendly voices, not too loud, but loud enough. They reached out and held a resident's hand or patted them gently on their shoulders for encouragement. They were remarkable in making sure that their residents felt loved.

I also observed how well the nurses and the nurse aides worked together; they were a team. They helped each other do whatever had to be done. Amazingly, they stayed focused on their work, in spite of the fact that the big screen TV was always on nearby them. It takes a lot of self-discipline to ignore all of the programs on a big colored TV. However, one day I found that the nurse aides were only human because they were actually watching the big screen. I saw them in a huddle focused on the TV at around 4:00 when I stepped out of the elevator that afternoon. They were very intent on what they were seeing.

As I walked past the rooms 200 to 210, I wondered what disastrous thing had happened in our nation or perhaps around the world. It had to be a newsbreak announcing something tragic. Just before I got to them, they broke away from the huddle and scattered. One walked to the linen closet to put away the towels she was holding. Two others reached for a resident's hands, pulled him up from the recliner, and began walking him down the other hallway. Two others pushed a resident's wheelchair to the bathroom for potty time. When I finally got to the big screen, it was on the Oprah Show so I figured that I had missed the newsbreak. Linda came along, and I asked what had happened. She said, "Nothing."

"You mean to say that nothing tragic or disastrous happened in the news just now? So, why were you all huddled together watching the big screen?" I asked her.

"We were just seeing what Oprah was wearing for her show today." And with that comment, Linda walked down the hallway to answer a call light.

On Sunday afternoons when I visited Mom, I enjoyed watching the big screen TV. Most residents seemed oblivious to the programming. So I found it amusing one afternoon when one resident said to another one, "Hey, Norma, that woman is blocking our view of the TV." I had been sitting with Mom all afternoon, and I observed that the woman had not been watching the TV. In fact, no one in the room was tuned in to what the TV had to offer. At least, everyone seemed expressionless. Since no one outwardly appeared to be interested in the TV, I found it interesting that one woman was upset that her view was blocked. I considered correcting the view-blocking problem by simply asking the guilty one to please move. Before I could do that, I heard the complaining voice say, " I don't know why they keep this TV on all day. No one ever watches it anyway. I certainly don't enjoy watching it." So I sat still.

The complainer continued by saying, "You would think it could be shut off when no one is watching it and give us some peace. Look at that, Norma! What nerve! That woman is still blocking our view. Well, Norma, someday they will figure things out. We just don't enjoy having that big TV on all afternoon . . . Norma, the Andy Griffith Show is on now. Let's watch it."

When you visit there often and at all hours of the day and night, you get the intimate view of things, and if you don't see it happen, you might just hear it happen. For instance, I heard a commotion around ten o'clock one evening that had to do with a mouse. Believe it or not, a mouse from the near-by farm decided to check out St. John. That was a mistake. The cleanliness was stifling, and I presume it went back to the farm.

The mouse was happily eating some cookies that had been stashed in a dresser drawer that was slightly ajar in Doris's room. When Doris saw the mouse, she put on her call light. Sara answered her call for help. Then Sara and Jodi chased it around the room. The floors were so polished that it was difficult for the mouse to make any traction to get away. It slid around for a while before it managed to escape its fate, but just barely.

As a mother and a homemaker, I recognized that the laundry tasks are enormous for a facility with one hundred thirty-nine beds, eight in assisted living, plus a daycare with thirty kids. Clothes are not just washed and dried, but they are also tagged for identity and mended before they make their way to the individual closets. With all of the laundry tasks to be done, I was impressed that they took the time and effort to wash Mom's big cloth doll. It was carefully washed and dried and returned to her looking just as cute as it always did.

It was understandable that no matter how careful they were in the laundry room, things ended up missing, just like they do at home. Mom's blue afghan went to the laundry, but it didn't come back again. Nurse Mary quickly substituted another afghan, a pink and blue one, very similar to Mother's blue one.

I was extremely impressed with the integrity of the staff. One day when I stopped at the nurse's station, nurse Mary said that she had something for me. She went to another room and came back with a white envelope. "Virginia, here is your mom's wedding ring. She can easily take it off her finger now that she is thinner. Once, we found it in her bedding. Another time, our cleaning lady found it on the floor beside her bed. I think that your mother would want you to have the ring now." Thanks to the honesty of the staff, I have Mom's wedding ring, which could easily have been stolen by someone lacking integrity.

In the days, weeks, months that followed, I continued to see God's blessing on my clothesline decision. Mom adjusted well to her new home at St. John Lutheran Home, and she seemed happy again. Nurse Mary said that Alzheimer's patients do better in a routine with regular meals and schedules. Mom was in the right place.

As often as I could, I took Mom for a walk inside the facility and when the weather was nice, for a walk outside the facility. We walked in the courtyard, and we watched the water fountain spraying water in the air. Mom sat on her favorite

bench, smiled and enjoyed the outdoors. No conversation
was necessary; she was just happy to be there. In fact, one day
Mom asked me to take a picture of her in the courtyard on her
favorite bench by the fountain. I got the impression she
thought she was vacationing at a fancy resort.

Quite often Mom and I sat in the lounge chairs at the end
of her hallway. One day while we were sitting in that spot,
Mom looked out the window and said, "There's the Pitman
farm." I was surprised to hear her say that. When I looked out
the window, I saw a farmhouse and a red barn. Indeed, it
looked a lot like the Pitman farm. Later when we walked into
Mom's room, I could see horses grazing in the pasture on the
hillside. I was so glad that Mom's bed was by the window so
she could view what she thought was the Pitman farm on a
daily basis. I was also glad that Mom was placed in the section
of the nursing home where she could see the Pitman farm
from the window at the end of the hallway.

Then the scripture verses came to my mind, "Don't let
your hearts be troubled. . . trust in God. . . I am going there
to prepare a place for you. . ." God had truly prepared a special place for Mom by placing her in just the right spot at St.
John Lutheran Home. I recalled the day when we actually
stood at the Pitman farm in Illinois. I was trying to fix her
mental confusion that day. It didn't work. Now God was
doing something far more wonderful. He gave her a view of
the Pitman farm every time she looked out the window. I
think it must have helped her feel at home, at last.

Paying Mom's Bills
Chapter Eight

A week after placing Mom at St. John Home, the financial reality of things hit me hard. How would we pay Mom's
bills? With one phone call to the nursing home on Monday,
Mom was placed there on Friday. It happened so quickly.
The emotional strain of it had overshadowed the question of
how we would pay Mom's bills. Since nursing home care is
expensive, the monthly bill would probably be a huge
amount. Who would pay the bill? I couldn't do it. My
brother couldn't do it. Who could?

Mom did not own any property. She had some money in
a savings account, but not much. She got a monthly social
security check, and that was something. She easily lived on her
social security check because her lifestyle was very simple. Her
social security check would pay some of the nursing home bill,
but who would pay the rest of it? Who would stand the gap?
And for how long?

When I mentioned my problem to Mary Lynn at the
nursing home, she told me to check into medical assistance,
and she encouraged me to meet with the Human Services for
my county as soon as possible. "Virginia, go ahead and apply
for assistance. See if your mom is eligible. You won't know
until you try."

I made an appointment with a social worker named Linda
at the Redwood County office in Redwood Falls. Linda listened patiently to me as I explained Mom's financial needs.
She gave me paperwork to fill out and asked for recent copies
of the bank statements of her savings and checking accounts.
"Virginia, I want you to make an appointment with the gal at
the front desk to see me in a week or so. Bring all of your

paperwork with you that day."

At my next visit with Linda, I presented her with every-thing that she needed to know. She ushered me into her office and opened Mom's file. She sat at her desk with a forward motion, and then she put on her eyeglasses and poured over the details of my reports. The long strips of calculator tape with folds of it on the floor indicated how busy she was with her case figures. For a long time, I studied her face to see if there was hope for Mom and for me. She was friendly but business-like, and I couldn't read her reactions so I had to wait for her to speak.

Without saying anything to me, she repositioned her swivel chair so that she could enter some figures into her calculator. Her fingers flew over the keys. My heart pounded inside me. What did the numbers mean? Finally, she looked up, removed her glasses, leaned back in her chair, and tapped her fingernails on her desk as she pondered something before she spoke to me. "From your preliminary figures, I think your mom will qualify, but I can't say for certain at this point. I will notify you by mail if your mom is eligible for our medical assistance. You will be hearing from me within a week."

Her answer wasn't a "no" but it wasn't a "yes" either. I would have to wait. Waiting was hard for me because it gave me time to think about it. Linda was obviously going to do some checking on the figures and the bank statements. What if she re-figured her formula and found a mistake? Her fingers were flying rather fast over the keys. What then? I needed to think positive thoughts about the situation; I had to keep telling myself that it was going to turn out fine. Mom's financial needs would be met. God was with us, and He would make a way.

Linda said that I would be hearing from her within a week. Each time I walked to our mailbox, I wondered about the expected letter. As the week came to a close, each time I sifted through our mail, I was excited when I saw anything with a large white business envelope. I expected it to be the letter that was promised to me. I keep thinking positive thoughts about how God would be taking care of things. Finally, the letter came. I saw the return address, Redwood County Human Services. I ripped it open and scanned the letter and focused my eyes on three wonderful words, "Ethel Bausch Qualifies." Yes, Redwood County would stand the gap. Mom's bills would be paid. Praise God!

Paperwork sometimes takes time to process. Eventually, another letter came to me and took me by surprise. It was from the Redwood County Human Services. Linda was writing to tell me that she could not be Mom's caseworker because St. John Lutheran Home was not in her county. She was transferring Mom's file to Brown County where it needed to be, and I would eventually be receiving a letter from Brown County Family Services telling me if Mom was eligible for medical assistance.

The tiny word "if" made me shudder. What if they refused Mom's case? What if Brown County didn't have as much funding for medical assistance? What would I do then? Would I have to transfer Mom to a nursing home in Redwood County? I was crossing bridges before I got to them. Waiting was hard for me. A week went by and no letter came.

Finally, I made a call to the Brown County office. "Do you have the file for Ethel Bausch?" I asked the receptionist.

"Let me check our case files. Hang on, please." A few minutes passed before she returned to the phone. "How did you spell that name?" "Hold on, please."

I was holding on . . . hanging on . . . waiting . . . for an answer.

"No, I don't have any file with that name. It must be on Cathy's desk, and she is on vacation this week, but she'll be back on Monday. I will leave a note for her to call you." And with those words the receptionist gave me a friendly good-bye.

A week passed with no phone call from Cathy. Since she had been on vacation, she probably needed time to catch up with her work. Should I call her? Or should I wait? I had to know the answer. Mom's first nursing home bill was on my desk by then. Her social security check would not cover it. What was I to do about that?

I picked up the phone and made the call. Just as I thought, the receptionist told me Cathy was desperately trying to catch up on her case files. When Cathy actually spoke to me, she assured me she would be notifying me within a week if Mom qualified. Again I heard that little word "if." Yes, I had been down this road before, but it wasn't any easier. What would happen to Mom if she didn't qualify? Who would pay Mom's medical bills? I had to make myself think positive thoughts. Surely, God would take care of things for us.

Finally, one day as I stood at our mailbox, I saw the business envelope with Brown County Human Services written in the left-hand corner. I ripped open the envelope, scanned the letter, and focused my eyes on three wonderful words, "Ethel Bausch Qualifies." Yes, Brown County would stand the gap. Mom's bills would be paid.

Every six months, I had to fill out paper work to renew Mom's eligibility. Admittedly, it was never that nerve wracking. Instead, it was just a procedure for me to follow. I sent in the information, and in a few days a letter came to me. I opened it to read the words, "Ethel Bausch Qualifies." No matter what happened after that, she always qualified for medical assistance. As Mom's condition worsened and her classification level changed, the cost for her care soared. God was faithful. Mom's bills were always paid. Her social security check paid for some of it, and Brown County paid for the rest of it.

Every dollar was paid. Every penny was paid. Until the day she died.

Creating Special Moments
Chapter Nine

Life is a day-by-day, moment-by-moment event. Thankfully, we don't know what is ahead of us, or we would be discouraged before we got to it.   Mom was a resident at St. John Lutheran Home for almost five years. Admittedly, it was a painful thing to see her decline, so the challenge was to look for the positives and to downplay the negatives. From the beginning, I was determined to stay involved. My visits with her were more important than ever.

Mom had this incredible, genuine smile. When she smiled, her brown eyes twinkled, and her whole face beamed with a deep-down smile that radiated her warmth. Little by little as we took the journey, I realized that Alzheimer's was stealing her smiles and replacing them with a blank, expressionless stare. How could I get her to smile for me? The answer was to create special moments for her.

For an Alzheimer's person, the present moment is the most important moment. There is no enjoyment in the anticipation of celebrating an event. Only the present moment counts. After it's over, it's gone from memory. My goal was to make the most of the present moment with Mom and hope to see her smile. As I visited her often, I discovered that little things made her smile, like taking her a chocolate chip cookie, a single carnation in a vase, a stuffed animal, or a balloon on a string. Little moments became special moments like being with her as we looked at old family photos, as we watched TV, as I read to her from a magazine, or as I wrote my Christmas cards.

She enjoyed walking outside in the courtyard, sitting on the bench and watching the water fountain spraying water in the air. When she could no longer walk, I pushed her wheelchair to another part of the nursing home so she could enjoy a change of scenery by looking at the courtyard below us. These were simple ordinary moments that brought her a sense of joy.

Naturally, I tried to make Mom's birthday a special time for her. Each year we celebrated in a different way. For her first birthday at her new home, our family had a birthday party to celebrate her eighty-fifth birthday. We invited the staff and the residents from her station to join us for cake, ice cream, balloons and presents. Even though we could see that Mom didn't realize that the celebration was in her honor, we were not discouraged. It was great to see her smile as she ate her cake and ice cream.

On her next birthday, I took her flowers, a balloon and several gift-wrapped packages. We had our own quiet party that day in her room, just Mom and I. Actually, that's how we spent the rest of her birthdays, in a quiet way in her room. She didn't realize it was her birthday. But that didn't matter. I felt fortunate when Mom just looked at me and smiled.

When my daughter got married, it wasn't possible to have Mom at the wedding because of her condition. It was heartbreaking for me to know that she missed such an important day in my life. Despite my sadness, I was determined to create a special moment for her. After the wedding was over, I took my daughter's wedding dress to the nursing home for Mom to see. Her little hands smoothed the material as she looked at it closely. Mom loved to sew in her younger years, and by having her touch the fabric of the dress, I created a moment of joy for her. I know that she didn't get the connection that the wedding dress was from her granddaughter's wedding. That was expected. At least, Mom and I had a special moment together.

When my son Charlie got married three years later, Mom's condition had worsened. She rarely spoke in those days. My daughter had made several floral arrangements for the wedding, and she suggested that I take one to Mom. I took one that was in an old fashioned pitcher, the kind that was once used as a pitcher and basin. I hoped that the antique pitcher would strike a chord within her. I was right. When she saw it, she perked up, and to my surprise, she said these words aloud, "Oh, pretty flowers!" That was her moment of joy. Her joy became my joy.

We usually spent our Christmas Eve at St. John Lutheran Home. Naturally, we took Mom's gifts to her and helped her open them while she smiled and enjoyed the evening with us. As we sang Christmas carols together with the staff, we helped make their evening a little brighter. One year for Christmas, I bought Mom a white sweatshirt with a striking picture of a cardinal on the front. I noticed that the staff always made a fuss over that sweatshirt whenever Mom was wearing it. The extra attention that Mom received because of the eye-catching red bird on her shirt was a delight to me. Mom was having special moments of attention, and I didn't have to be there to create those moments for her.

I often took Mom fresh flowers. She always smiled and said, "Oh, for me?" Roses and carnations were her favorites. I hoped that the flowers would remind her of the days when she raised them in her own flower gardens. Taking her a flower was always a perk for her, even when she was no longer able to speak. Instead, she just smiled and shrugged her shoulder in a way that said to me, "Oh, for me?" Fresh flowers were a great way to create a moment of joy.

Whenever I visited Mom, I always checked her mail to see if there was anything to open and read aloud to her. My brother's wife, Anne, was faithful to remember Mom often by sending her gifts and greeting cards to cheer her. Anne never missed a holiday, and her three children were faithful, too. They all knew the kind of cards that would please Mom, cards with kittens, birds, or flowers. A simple greeting card created a moment of joy.

Whenever I was wearing something red, Mom noticed it. She would say to me, "You look so pretty." She liked seeing me in the color red. Later, I returned the favor. When she was wearing red, I always said to her, "Mom, you look so pretty." That was a perk for her. I loved complimenting her because she shrugged her shoulder in that curious way of hers and smiled so warmly. That's how she always responded to a compliment.

As Mom's condition worsened, and she was unable to speak or to respond at all, I discovered that she reacted to me whenever I hugged her and told her, "Mom, you look so pretty." I saw a slight response, ever so slight as it was. I saw a little shrug of her shoulders. Then I knew she was aware of what I was saying to her. Her little shoulder movement told me she understood what I had said to her.

On the first Mother's Day when she was at St. John Lutheran Home, I didn't take her flowers. As I rushed off to visit her that day, I felt guilty that I had not ordered her a special bouquet. However, I knew that I could still make a great day for her if I was a little creative. Spontaneously, I reached into a dresser drawer and took out an old purse that originally belonged to her mother. How perfect! I would create a special moment by having her connect with her mother. It worked beautifully.

The purse was a small fabric handbag filled with keepsakes that belonged to her mother. When Mom opened the clasp of the handbag, she found several things inside that she could take out and hold in her hands, tiny gloves for tiny hands, fancy combs that were used in her mother's hair, a ring box with an opal ring inside, a small envelope with a note in her mother's handwriting, and a small portrait of her parents. Very carefully, she took out everything; very carefully she put back everything. She smiled as she did it. She enjoyed smelling and touching everything. For a long time Mom sat at the table in the dining area of the day room and enjoyed the purse.

Mom was only fourteen years old when she lost her mother as she died suddenly from complications of surgery. The remembrance of her mother still lingered in her mind in spite of her Alzheimer's. Mom often said that her favorite memory of her mother was seeing her mom brush her long brown hair, and then arrange it on top of her head using the combs to keep it in place. Such was the style back then. Her mother was a dainty woman. We could tell by the tiny gloves, the tiny opal ring, and the dainty handwriting. As we looked at the small wedding portrait of her parents, we could easily see that her mom was a pretty woman and her father was quite handsome. I was so pleased with Mom's response to the purse that I took it to her every Mother's Day thereafter.

Even though Mom's condition had worsened in a year's time, when I took the purse to her on Mother's Day, she tenderly took out everything and carefully placed each thing on the table. She slowly put everything back into the purse. We didn't converse about the purse because Mom was not capable of conversation anymore. I sat quietly by her and let her spend as much time as she wanted to spend. It was heart warming to know that she was connecting with the Mother that she once knew long ago. When she was finished, she said, "Mmmm . . . that was so good." The expression in her voice sounded like she had just eaten a dish of ice cream.

When I took Mom the purse on the next Mother's Day, I had to help her open the clasp because her little hands could no longer do that. Very slowly, she reached into the purse and gently took out the precious things. She held each thing in her hand for a long time, and then she placed it on the table. Carefully, she put each thing back into the purse, taking time to smell each of the keepsakes from her mother. Mom didn't say a word as she enjoyed the purse, but when she was finished, she made this sound, "Mmmm...." I knew that she was pleased. Enjoying the purse was just as good as eating a butterscotch sundae.

Showing my mom the purse on Mother's Day gave me another idea; I made a special memory purse for her to enjoy daily. The purse had several compartments that I filled with some of Mom's things, interesting yet ordinary things from her past. Mom could hold each thing in her hand and feel and smell it before putting it back into the purse. She enjoyed things such as a bar of Yardley Soap, some of her old jewelry, a small cookbook, her measuring spoons, her guitar pick, some old photos of her sister and her brother, a handkerchief with her name Ethel embroidered on it, and a deck of cards. I gave the memory purse to the nurses, and they gave it to Mom when she became restless. She loved her memory purse, and the things inside it often brought a smile to her face.

When Mariah our first grandchild was born, I ached for my mom. She missed that important event in our lives. I took her pictures of Mariah and told her about the tiny brown-eyed, brown-haired baby. Mom loved seeing babies, so she reacted noticeably to the pictures of Mariah. But there was no way for her to know that she was looking at her great-granddaughter. At least we saw her smile.

My daughter and I had the joy of taking my little grand-daughter Mariah to meet her great-grandmother Ethel on Mother's Day of 1999. My daughter Christy carefully placed Mariah on Mom's lap so she could hold her with our help. Then we took lots of pictures of the four generations. Mom rarely spoke words in those days, so we were surprised when Mom said softly, "Pretty baby" as she smiled that wonderful smile of hers. That was Mom's last Mother's Day.

Creating special moments for Mom always gave me a warm, fuzzy feeling inside. It was worth the thought and the effort I put into it. My mom was still my mom even though her mental and physical abilities were declining. Little by little, during those five years at St. John Lutheran Home, I learned to adapt to the new version of Mom, and I tried my best to make the most of it by constantly looking for different ways to connect with her.

Eventually, in the lowest phase of Alzheimer's disease, Mom's condition was so weak she could not respond to me. I continued to talk to her knowing she would not respond verbally. When I looked for other signs, other body language, most of the time, I couldn't detect any physical response from her. But as I sat by her side, I felt Mom communicate within me in a silent way. Somehow, I always heard her voice saying, "Virginia, I'm still me. I'm trapped inside of me. I can't respond. I know that you are trying to connect with me. Don't ever give up on me. I'm still me."

A Second Childhood
Chapter Ten

Having a grandchild is a wonderful thing because it's a chance to experience the thrills of another childhood. I was too busy to enjoy my children's passage through childhood because I gave birth to five of them in ten years time, and understandably, life was rather hectic for me. When our first grandchild Mariah was born, my husband and I became conscious of the fact that we now have a second chance to watch a child grow and develop. The second childhood called "grandchildren" is a blessing that God designed for us to enjoy.

Sadly enough, Alzheimer's disease takes the person to a second childhood. Instead of growing and developing, Mom was declining and failing. Her mind, her personality, and her bodily functions were going in reverse, from child to toddler, and from toddler to infant. Alzheimer's is an unexpected twist in the normal aging process; the irony is childhood instead of old age. Eventually, it means diapers, bibs, spoon feedings, wheelchairs and geri chairs.

Mercifully, the Alzheimer's second childhood does not happen overnight because it is a slow progression. When Mariah was born, she didn't grow up over night. She was a baby for a long time. She crawled before she walked. She babbled and vocalized a long time before she talked. Childhood takes time and so does the second childhood. Granted, the second childhood can never be like watching a child maturing and developing. It's not going to be the excitement of the first word, the first step, or the first time riding a bike.

Fortunately, there are some excellent manuals on the market now explaining Alzheimer's, and there are several books that teach how to relate to the person going through the second childhood. In fact, I am always learning something new about Alzheimer's as I read and study the subject. Lately, I learned how effective music is for Alzheimer's people. It speaks to them by energizing them or it speaks to them in a calming way. Most importantly, music is a tremendous pathway for connecting with an unresponsive Alzheimer's person. I have heard so many heart-warming stories about how music made the difference. The unresponsive suddenly became responsive when someone played the piano, played a CD, or sang directly to them.

Recently, I heard this wonderful story. An Alzheimer's woman was silent for many years. The nursing home staff was absolutely astonished when they actually heard her sing one day. A visitor brought a guitar and knelt beside her wheelchair and sang "Amazing Grace." By the time the vocalist reached the second verse, the Alzheimer's woman joined her by singing the words, and together they finished the hymn. Music appears to take a different pathway throughout the brain. Alzheimer's people can sing and relate to music when they are totally unable to speak a word.

When an Alzheimer's person has to be placed in a nursing home, it's a very difficult time for the family. The temptation for some families is to withdraw because it is painful to face that situation. Some families choose to "drop them off at the nursing home" so to speak, and they don't return until the person dies. How can they do that? They justify it by this kind of reasoning, "The Mom that I once knew is gone. I've lost her already. She died a long time ago."

No! No! No! That kind of thinking is not true. She didn't die. She entered her second childhood. In fact, she needs her family more than ever, she needs their involvement, and she needs their love. To abandon her during the second childhood is just as serious as abandoning a small child.

Recently, as I was having lunch in town, I heard a man seated at a table near me say this about his Alzheimer's neighbor, "Joe's at the nursing home. He doesn't know beans. No reason to visit him now." No! No! No! That kind of thinking is not true. Joe is still Joe. He's in his second childhood. He needs visitors more than ever.

How do you know how to treat a person in his second childhood? Observe how the trained staff at the nursing home does it. That's how I learned how to treat Mom. Even though Alzheimer's is a second childhood, one must never call the person a child; one must never make the person feel like he is being treated like a child. One must never talk down to the person. One must always treat the person with dignity and talk to him in a positive and uplifting manner. Alzheimer's people are adults, not children. Dignity must always prevail.

There is a biblical expression that goes like this, "A little child shall lead them." Observe how little children relate to Alzheimer's people. They smile at them. They talk to them. They crawl upon their lap. They show them their toys. They are totally uninhibited. That's how we must be. We must be open and natural around them.

Just as a child needs praise and positive reinforcement, Alzheimer's children have a great need for positive reinforcement and praise. Look for words that praise them for whatever they can accomplish or achieve. Tell them so.

"Great job of winning at Bingo, Mom." or "Mom, I heard you helped to fold some towels today. Good for you." or "You actually made this Christmas tree in activities today? Good job, Mom!" or "I like the picture you colored today in your coloring book, Mom." or "Good girl, Mom. You ate all of your food at dinner tonight." or "You went to a picnic today? How fun!' or "That's great you can walk to the end of the hallway and back again with the help of your nurse aides. The exercise is wonderful for you. Good job, Mom." And so on.

Most children are happier living in a routine, knowing what to expect each day. Alzheimer's people do better in a routine, also. Change is difficult for them. I noticed the reluctance of the nursing staff to change rooms for Mom; they realized that a simple change from one room to another would be upsetting for her, and they did it only when it was absolutely necessary. How do you deal with a major change like helping them to adjust to life at the nursing home? You can look to a child. Let a child teach you what to do. For instance, our granddaughter can show you the way.

When our granddaughter Mariah was two years old, she came to stay with us for a week while her parents, Chad and Christy, vacationed in Branson, Missouri. My husband and my sons were worried. They were certain that Mariah would stand at the window with her nose pressed against the glass and cry for her mommy and daddy for the whole week. I wasn't concerned at all. I was confident that she would adapt quickly. And she did.

Mariah came with her favorite blanket, her puppy pillow, her Groovy Girl doll and her sippy cup. We created a happy zone for her with pleasant smiles and cheery voices. No loud noises were allowed to upset her. She needed a calm, soft and fuzzy world around her. We did just fine.

When Mom went to St. John Lutheran Home, we did everything we could to make her feel safe and secure. We took along the blue afghan that Anne had made for her; it served as her security blanket. Even though she no longer played her organ; having it in her room made her feel safe. On her dresser, I placed numerous old photos of Mom and Dad and of my brother and me. I also made a special album with pictures of Mom when she was a little girl, and I included photos of her parents and her siblings. The goal was to create a happy memory zone for Mom, one in which she felt comfortable.

When Mariah came to stay with us, we spoke gently to her using her first name. We held her, hugged her and loved her. At St. John Lutheran Home, the staff spoke gently to Mom always using her first name while making eye contact with her. They never talked down to her. They treated her like an adult. They often touched her hand or arm as they talked to her. They used a pleasant tone of voice and smiled at her often. They treated her with utmost dignity. She was in a place that felt warm, cozy and friendly to her. No loud noises. It was calm and peaceful.

Mom did well with that kind of attention and care.

Since Mariah was a soft-spoken dainty two-year-old, it took time for her to warm up to us that week. The more she felt at ease around us, the more she spoke aloud. She knew just how to communicate her needs and wishes to us by saying only a few words. "Come...meer...Nana." Then she took my hand and led me to the kitchen and pointed to the sack of Oreo cookies on top of the kitchen counter. "Watch Blues...Nana." She found her favorite Blues Clues video and popped it into the VCR. Then she gestured for me to sit with her to watch it. Sometimes, she crawled on Papa's lap with her favorite book, *The Mouse Cookie*. He knew what she meant. He read her the story.

Communication is everything. Mariah had no trouble communicating her wishes. If it wasn't with words, it was with gestures and facial expressions. Granted, when Mariah was born, she did not automatically know how to talk; she had to learn to talk. It was a gradual process for her. When Mom lost her ability to talk, it was a gradual process. When I first took Mom to St. John Lutheran Home, she could read anything you asked her to read, and she could write her name correctly. True, she was confused about people, time, and places, but she could still converse with me.

Slowly, her ability to communicate deteriorated. At first, I noticed she used a wrong word. One day, she was speaking to my youngest son and she said, "Such a pretty red closet you are wearing today." She made that comment just as one of the nurse aides was putting fresh linens in the closet near us. Mom meant to say to Tom, "Such a pretty red jacket you are wearing today."

As time went on, she spoke with strangely unconnected words that made no sense to us. Her facial expression and her tone of voice showed how frustrated she was with her inability to say what she wanted to say. When she couldn't communicate with words, we studied her body language, like her curious shrug of her shoulder or some other familiar expression of hers that hinted at what she might be trying to tell us.

Little children learn to speak by using a language that only they understand. Mom's speech eventually became garbled with a long, steady, senseless babbling of sounds along with some familiar words. It was a strange language to us. When she managed to say something clear, it was a surprise. One evening, she rattled on and on for at least an hour as she sat in her geri chair. Finally, something clear came out of her mouth. She said, "My legs are cold." I put her afghan over her to warm her.

When babies are babies, they coo at first, and then they learn to vocalize sounds. They usually babble on and on for a long time before they say their first word. Mom eventually got to the stage when she babbled and vocalized in sounds; no longer could she speak in words. Instead, she spoke in a non-stop chatter of various vowel and consonant sounds. Eventually, she stopped speaking altogether. She vacillated from having an anxious facial expression to sitting there in utter silence with a blank stare.

I remember how excited my daughter was when Mariah first started walking around furniture; it wasn't long before she was walking on her own. When Mom first went to St. John Lutheran Home, she walked on her own with her walking stick to steady her when she needed it. Then one day, the walking stick was put in the upper part of her closet on top of her blue suitcase because it was no longer safe for her to walk with it; she needed people to walk with her. Then the nurses or nurse aides walked on each side of her. Eventually, walking that way became too difficult for Mom.

After that, Mom was confined to her wheelchair, managing only a few steps at a time like going from her wheelchair to her bed or to the bathroom. Eventually, her wheelchair was changed to a geri chair, a giant "infant seat" capable of being upright or reclined, so that she could be placed in a reclined position because of osteoporosis in her lower back; it was painful for her to sit upright for a very long time.

How many scrapes and bruises did Mariah have by the

time she was two years old? Countless! Actually, she made a trip to the emergency room to have stitches in her face next to her eye when she fell as a toddler. Mom also had bumps and bruises because she fell a few times. And Mom also made a trip to the emergency room after falling.

The nursing staff did everything they could to keep Mom safe, but Mom's dementia made it extremely difficult to protect her from falling. Thankfully, Mom never broke any bones; she just suffered bruises. The staff used bed alarms and chair alarms to alert them when Mom was in danger of falling. Understandably enough, it was impossible to watch her every single moment.

When I first saw Mom at mealtime at the small dining area in the day room by the nurse's station, she was wearing a bib, a large terry cloth bib. Actually, she wasn't the only one; all of the residents wore bibs. It was a rather strange thing seeing adults wearing bibs, but eventually, I got used to the idea. When Mom first arrived at St. John Lutheran Home, she fed herself, and she was a good eater; granted, it took awhile for her to eat because she enjoyed each morsel of food, just like she enjoyed her ice cream.

One day my heart sank when I visited St. John Lutheran Home at suppertime. I saw Jodi spoon-feeding Mom her supper. I stopped and observed the process. As Jodi brought the spoon to her face, Mom opened her mouth, just like a toddler does, and happily ate the food. The words of Dr. Schmitz, warning me of a day when Mother could no longer feed herself, were finally true. Mom could no longer pick up a fork to feed herself.

Mom's food was chopped to make it possible for her to chew it. Then her food was ground so she could eat it with no problems. Finally, her food was mashed and pureed to make it easier for her to swallow and digest. Liquids had to be thickened for her. Eventually, even her drinking water was thickened to the consistency of pudding so she wouldn't choke trying to drink it. Swallowing became a serious problem for Mom in the final segment of her second childhood. Understandably, by then she was like an infant.

Having Mariah with us for a week meant my husband and I had to slow our pace. We patiently hooked and unhooked Mariah into her car seat wherever we went that week. Our schedule adapted around her schedule, her naptime and her bedtime. It was potty time, snack time, suppertime, bath time and bedtime. We were exhausted at the end of the week. We weren't used to taking care of a two-year-old.

Since Alzheimer's disease is a second childhood, it makes them like little people again. Everything needs to be done at a slower pace. There is need for lots of patience when working with them. While eating their meals, sometimes they spill food, or sometimes they refuse to eat. Sometimes they mix and play with their food. Sometimes they pour their milk over everything on their plate.

They are like children again. They do what children do. Sometimes, they spontaneously take off their clothes. Sometimes, they wear inappropriate clothing.Sometimes, they wear no clothing. Sometimes, they wear someone else's clothing and think it's theirs. Sometimes, they wet or soil themselves. Then diapers are needed. Help is needed to go to the toilet. Potty training in reverse takes place. Diapers eventually prevail.

When Mom first went to St. John Lutheran Home, she could dress herself and toilet herself. When that changed, her nurse aides helped her. St. John Lutheran Home is very particular about how often they toilet their residents, how often they change diapers and how often they reposition them at night. Mom always had a fresh, clean scent whenever I visited her. She never had a bedsore in the time she was there. Her nurse aides were meticulous with her personal hygiene.

Children are sometimes naughty. Parents have to discipline and train children so they grow up to be responsible adults. Alzheimer's children are not trainable. No longer are they capable of being reasoned with, and they can be quite stubborn. At times, it is difficult to handle them. Sometimes they are naughty. They resist the ones who are doing their personal hygiene. They refuse to open their mouths for teeth brushing. They are combative with anyone trying to wash them or with anyone trying to give them their medications. They hit, spit, kick, pinch, scream and cry. Yes, they can be naughty and rather nasty to deal with when the dementia takes them to a second childhood. Fortunately, trained staff members know how to deal with these issues.

Once when I was visiting Mom, she was holding her doll that she always treated so tenderly. Then suddenly her mood changed; she grabbed it, squeezed it hard, and shook it repeatedly. I was surprised at her behavior; it was a streak of meanness that I wasn't accustomed to seeing. Sometimes, Alzheimer's people say mean things to their loved ones. Mom never did that to us.

Granddaughter Mariah has a wonderful imagination because her mother loves to play along with her as they fantasize about things. In fact, Mariah has an imaginary play friend that she calls Mattie. I am glad that I eventually learned to play along with Mom just like my daughter does with Mariah. For instance, one day I asked Mom what she had done that day. "Oh, I helped my mother wash clothes today. Yesterday, I helped Dad clean chickens."

So I responded by saying to her, "Well, you must be tired after doing all of that work." Then Mom told me she could rest tomorrow because her family was planning to go on a picnic by the lake.

Little children can say and do the cutest things. As parents or as grandparents, we are always looking for that moment when they make us smile, better yet, when they make us laugh. When Mom was in her second childhood, I looked for the humor of things, the unexpected amusing moments that sometimes come our way.

One day a resident walked up to me and surprised me with these words, "I'll gladly help you find something. Most of our sale items are in this aisle, but we do have a few things in the basement of the store." The woman had worked for many years as a clerk in the Ben Franklin Store. She was still clerking.

That incident reminded me of a story someone shared with me about an Alzheimer's man who had been in the furniture business all of his life. One day, he was mysteriously pushing the furniture from his nursing home room into the hallway at five o'clock in the morning. When the nurse asked him what he was doing, he answered, "Today is Crazy Days. I'm getting ready for the sidewalk sale."

Mom ate her meals in the small dining area by the nurse's station. A nurse aide usually fed her, but sometimes I did it. One evening when I was spoon-feeding Mom, I heard a woman's voice say, "I'm going to Bermuda." That's a nice thought! One of the nurse aides is going to Bermuda on a vacation. A little bit later, I heard the voice again, "I'm going to Bermuda." That was not a nurse aide speaking. It was a resident. A third time, I heard it, "I'm going to Bermuda." It came from the direction of Lena who I didn't think could talk. Well, she did that evening because she said it again, "I'm going to Bermuda on the good ship Lollipop."

One evening, I was doing my Christmas cards while Mom sat by me at the dining table. I could see she enjoyed being with me. Sara told me it was fine if Mom stayed up past her usual bedtime to be with me. Finally, all of the residents were put to bed, except one little woman sitting at the table next to us. She had been quietly sitting there all evening. Finally, she broke her silence by saying, " Well, this is the last time I'm taking the bus. I've been sitting here in this bus station for hours."

Little kids love to see themselves in a mirror. Their antics are laughable as they make gestures and expressions while they see their own reflection. Not so with Alzheimer's children. I learned to avoid putting Mother in front of a mirror. She did not recognize herself in the mirror, and it hurt her feelings because she thought she was much younger. Of course, the mirror revealed her real age.

I heard a story about an Alzheimer's woman who was very

upset with a stranger's presence in her bedroom. When she led her daughter down the hallway to her bedroom and to the full-length mirror hanging on her closet door, she finally said, "There's that stranger," as she pointed to her own image in the mirror.

Childhood goes rather quickly because everyday is a day to discover something new. When it comes to remembering Mariah's childhood, it will be fun because her mother is doing a Creative Memories scrapbook for her. It will show all the aspects of her growing up because her mother is constantly updating it with pictures and notes about her childhood.

When my mother was in her Alzheimer's childhood, I took a few photos of her, I wrote a few notes about her, and I made a small scrapbook about her. I keep it on the top shelf of my bedroom closet. I seldom look at the scrapbook because it's too painful. Mom's second childhood was also her "long good-bye."

The Doll
Chapter Eleven

When my granddaughter Mariah had her first birthday, we gave her a soft teddy bear with a dark blue ribbon around his neck. We named him Bailey. He was the perfect size for her to cuddle when she went to sleep in her crib or when she sat in her car seat. For Christmas, we gave her a large brown and white puppy pillow, which she takes everywhere, along with her Groovy Girl doll.

When Mom was in her second childhood, she spent many hours in her geri chair in the day room. Her hands were restless, and her facial expression was anxious and troubled. She needed something to hold in her arms. She needed a teddy bear or a puppy pillow or a Groovy Girl doll. I tried to find her something that she would like. I bought her several dolls and some stuffed animals, some large and some small. One particular one was a soft, furry white dog with a pug face and a big red bow. Since she liked red, I thought she would take to it, but she didn't.

You can imagine my surprise, when one day I learned that she had found something on her own. Marlys, the director of activities from St. John Lutheran Home, called me one day with some interesting news about Mom. "Virginia, your mom has claimed a doll from our department. She loves holding and cuddling it."

"Really? Marlys, tell me about the doll."

"It's a big doll and light as a feather for her to hold. It has long braids and a pretty face. Your mom loves it!"

"Where can I get one like it? I want her to have her own doll."

"Go to Redwood Falls. That's where I bought the doll."

That was interesting! Mom had found her own doll to comfort her. And I had the strange experience of buying my mother a doll so she could play with it. The doll's lightweight fabric made it squeezeably soft and washable, too. It had blue eyes, a small nose, and a cute smile embroidered on the cloth face. The doll was wearing a bonnet, a dress with lace and ruffles, white pantaloons, and blue shoes.

Essentially, Mom bonded with her doll, as she constantly mothered it by caressing its face, holding it close to her, affectionately straightening the lace, and stroking the long braids of yarn. For two years, it was her constant companion as she lapsed deeper into Alzheimer's childhood. The doll sat on her lap as she was being spoon-fed her meal; the doll went to bed with her at night; ultimately, the doll was beside her on the bed the day she died.

When my granddaughter Mariah returned to her parents after staying with us that week, my husband teased her parents by saying, "In another week or two, Mariah would have forgotten who you are." We knew that he was just teasing, but it posed an interesting thought. Would Mariah forget her parents if she were away from them too long? I was having those same thoughts about Mom. Would Mom forget me now that the Alzheimer's journey was taking so long?

I looked for signs that she still knew me. Whenever I walked into the dayroom to visit her, she always looked at me and kept eye contact with me until I was by her side. That was a strong assurance for me, until I noticed that she reacted that way to some of her caregivers at St. John Lutheran Home. Then I was worried. One day I asked nurse Mary if she could assure me that my mom hadn't forgotten who I was. "Do you think Mom still remembers me?"

"I wish I could answer that for you, Virginia. I think she knows you, but it's difficult to say for certain with her Alzheimer's condition."

I wrestled with this issue for a long time. It was painful for me to visit her and wonder if she had totally forgotten me.

I hoped that in some way she still remembered me. As her condition worsened, I found myself trying to make peace with things. Mom would never want to forget me, but she was powerless to stop it from happening if it did. Eventually, I realized that I needed to surrender to the situation; I needed to make peace with it by accepting it. Mom was trapped inside a body that was failing her and with a mind that wasn't functioning normally. There was nothing that I could do to change it.

Every three months St. John Lutheran Home invited me to join them for a care conference to discuss Mom's changing condition. Nurse Mary was there to tell me about her latest medications and any physical problems that she was having. Linda, the registered dietician, explained her eating intake and her weight gain or loss. Marlys from the activities department reported on what level of participation Mom had with the activities program.

One day as I was waiting for my care conference to begin, I chatted with a social worker and I asked him this question, "Linus, can a mother actually forget her child?" He knew my mother was suffering with Alzheimer's. Even though he wished to comfort me, he had no answer to my problem. "I really can't answer that, Virginia. Maybe someday you'll find the answer," he said as he headed for his office.

As he walked away, I stood for a while in the hallway and fondly thought about that memorable evening at home when my mother spoke my name. The night before she came to St. John Lutheran Home, I heard her loud whispers and out of curiosity I crawled across the living room floor to discover that she was praying. That's when she said "Virginia" aloud. That seemed like a long time ago, and indeed it was, because three years had passed.

Finally, it was my turn for the care conference. I walked into the room and sat at the conference table trying to look cheerful, trying to cover my inward sadness. When the door closed in the conference room, I knew they were ready to begin. Nurse Mary gave her report. Linda, the dietician, gave her report. Marlys, the director of activities, gave her report. Mom was doing well. There wasn't much else to discuss that day. But just before we were ready to disband from the meeting, Marlys had something interesting to tell me about Mother.

"By the way, I was on station three south yesterday, and I stopped to observe your mother for a while. I watched her holding her doll and mothering it so tenderly. For a long time, she was lovingly caressing its face. Finally, I spoke to your mother, and I told her that she had a pretty baby in her arms. Your mom smiled at me when I told her that."

"Marlys, did she make any other response?" I was hoping Mom did more than just smile at her.

"I asked your mom to tell me her baby's name."

"Do you think Mom understood what you were asking her, Marlys?"

"Yes, she made eye contact with me, and she was alert. As she held her doll close to her, she said your name, Virginia."

"What? She said my name? She actually said my name? Why, that's wonderful news! Thank you for sharing that story!" I tried to keep back the tears as I dabbed my eyes with a tissue. Suddenly, I knew that I had the answer to my problem. Alzheimer's disease may be strong, but it couldn't break my bond with my mother. Mom had not forgotten me. Her doll was not a doll, rather it was her baby, and I was that baby. I could rest in this assurance every time I saw her mothering her doll. I would always be her Virginia.

Amazingly, Mom never stopped being my mother. She gave me a special love pat one day because I was hurting. When you are a child, your mother always feels your pain. When she gives you a little love pat to console you, it's understandable. That's what mother's do. But when your mother, who is like a child, senses your pain and gives you a love pat to console you, it's totally remarkable.

I was devastated by something, but I was covering my hurt until I saw her reclined in the geri chair that afternoon. She was awake, and she made eye contact with me. She said nothing the whole time that I was with her. I didn't expect her to say anything to me because I knew that she couldn't. I was thankful that she would never know the details of why I was hurting that day. Alzheimer's would keep her from hearing it.

On that Sunday afternoon, I was relieved and glad that the day room by the nurse's station was empty and quiet. That's when Mom and I had this special moment together. As I walked to her side, I felt tears coming down my face, so I knelt beside her, buried my face in her lap, and sobbed for a while. Then, I felt someone pat me gently on the top of my head. I looked up to see who was patting me, expecting to see a nurse or nurse aide. Instead, it was Mom.

Despite her failing condition, she understood my pain and my tears, and she reached out to comfort me. Her arms were stiff, but somehow she managed to move one of them to me and gently pat my head, as if to say, "I love you." For a suspended moment, I was her child again. Although she couldn't speak to me that day, I heard her words to me anyway, the usual ones that she said when I was a little girl, "There, there, Virginia, you'll be fine."

Now that Mom is gone, I treasure her doll, and I treasure the bittersweet memory of her love pat that day. Today as I write this story, Mom's doll is on the white dresser in our upstairs spare bedroom. I will always have it to hold in my arms and remind me that my mother never forgot me.

Pink Nail Polish
Chapter Twelve

When two-year old Mariah stayed with us for a week when her parents were away on a vacation, she brought her suitcase filled with her things. Her mother had neatly packed in a Ziploc bag her cosmetics, including nail polish, her hairbrush, and her hair ribbons. I noticed that Mariah had a special fondness for the plastic bag. Whenever she felt like it, she took the bag out of her suitcase and found a quiet place behind our living room sofa. When she was seated on the floor, she unzipped the plastic bag and took out everything. One by one, she carefully put the hair ribbons on the carpet beside her. Then each elastic ponytail band was carefully placed next to the ribbons. Then she brushed her hair with her hairbrush and smiled.

Last of all, she looked at the bottle of nail polish. She didn't try to open the polish. She just looked at it and smiled, as she said the word "Mommy." Mariah missed her mother, and she was connecting to her mother by touching the hair ribbons and the nail polish. She was remembering the times when her mother brushed her hair, put in hair ribbons, and painted her fingernails. She liked the way her mommy made her feel pretty.

My son Charlie and his wife Heidi stopped for a short visit on that Sunday afternoon when Mariah was with us. It was obvious to all of us that Mariah was getting quite homesick for her parents, because she was very sad as she held her hair ribbons and nail polish close to her.

When Heidi walked into the room, she tenderly gathered Mariah onto her lap and said to her, "Let's comb your hair and put in a red pony tail." Mariah looked at the bottle of nail polish while Heidi fixed her hair. "Let's paint your nails." Then Heidi painted her nails a pinkish lavender color that sparkled. "Now go like this!" Heidi told her to hold her arms out straight and to spread her fingers apart. "See how pretty you are." Mariah understood the meaning of Heidi's words about feeling pretty because she smiled as she looked at her newly painted fingernails.

When I was a little girl, I loved to sit on my mother's lap and open her purse to look at her makeup. Mom had facial powder and a powder puff that she used on her face. I dabbed the puff on my face, imitating the way she did it. The rouge was in a small container that Mom let me open with her help. Sometimes, we dabbed a little on my checks, and we also dabbed a little of her red lipstick on my lips so that I could feel pretty.

Like most of the women of her times, Mom wore make-up when she dressed up and wanted to feel pretty. She seldom went to a beauty parlor because she did her own hair. Mom's hair always looked nice because her hair was naturally curly. She never had a perm; she didn't need it. As a young woman, she had dark brown hair, almost black, to go with her dark brown eyes. With age, her hair turned to a salt and pepper look, and then it turned pure white. Mom's pretty white hair was truly her crown of glory in her senior years.

Mom didn't fuss with a lot of fancy skin creams over the years like most women do, and, amazingly, her face didn't have the wrinkles that usually accompany a woman in her eighties. I don't know how that happened to her. Granted, she had lots of brown spots, but she didn't have the wrinkles like she should have had for her age. Oh yes, the skin under her chin sagged and fell, much to her disgust, but basically her face looked young for her age. Her skin was usually a beautiful tan color because she easily tanned in the outdoors.

As far as nail polish goes, I don't recall Mom using bright colors on her nails. Rather, she preferred the clear color, and the kind that promised to harden her nails. She liked her nails to be longer, not too long, but long enough.

When I became Mom's caregiver, I was in charge of all of her personal needs including her hygiene. For a while, I made use of our bathroom and shower next to our family room in our basement. A shower was convenient for washing her hair and all of the rest of her at the same time. Unfortunately, she hated the shower, and she cried when I washed her hair. As time went on, it was increasingly difficult for her to use our narrow steps that led to the basement, so I used our upstairs bathroom that had a bathtub. At bath time, I usually helped her into the bathtub and supervised her like I did for my youngsters when they took a bath. She enjoyed her bath and didn't cry until it was time for me to shampoo her hair. I tilted her head backwards into my arm and gently washed her hair.

One day, she no longer had the strength to get out of the tub, and she sat there looking at me for help. It took all my strength to help her to stand again so that she could climb out of the tub with my assistance. That was the last time I allowed her to sit in the bathtub. From that time on, I could only have her stand in the bathtub.

With a large pitcher, I poured water over her body and simulated the effect of her being in a shower. Mom's posture had a slight bend forward because of her osteoporosis, and her one leg was actually two inches shorter than her other leg as a result of her hip surgery. What a strange sight it must have been of me pouring water over a bent and wrinkled old woman standing in the bathtub on a mat so she would not slip and fall. Strange as it was, no one saw us!

Mom was a very private person about having her bath. While the rest of the family was gone to church, I could devote myself exclusively to her personal needs. One Sunday morning as my husband and my sons left for church, I felt very low because I missed going to church on a regular basis. That morning, I felt rather guilty about missing church because Mom's personal care was my Sunday morning routine. I wondered what God thought about me missing church.

When Mom's bath time was over, she was exhausted, so she crawled into her bed in our living room and took a little nap while I prepared our Sunday dinner. Then, I took a few minutes to sit in my favorite corner of my big brown sofa to read from my daily devotional booklet, *Our Daily Bread*. I felt like God was speaking to me when I read a poem written by Ruth Harms Calkin, entitled "I Wonder."

In her wonderful poem, Ruth Harms Calkin paints the picture of our natural enthusiasm for serving God in the limelight, in church, Sunday school, Bible studies, and fellowships. Then she artistically raises the question of what would we do if God called us to serve Him in a place where no one saw us, day after day, perhaps month after month. How would we act then? Ruth Harms Calkin pictured my situation amazingly well. Printed with her permission, here is what she wrote. . .

I Wonder

You know, Lord,
How I serve You
With great emotional fervor
In the limelight.
You know how eagerly
I speak for You
At a women's club.

You know how I effervesce
When I promote
A fellowship group.
You know my genuine enthusiasm
At a Bible study.

But how would I react, I wonder,
If You pointed to a basin of water
And asked me to wash
The calloused feet
Of a bent and wrinkled old woman
Day after day,
Month after month,
In a room where nobody saw
And nobody knew.

When I read those words to the poem, I was reminded once again of how personal God can be. He knew my thoughts that morning as I questioned my priorities, and He answered me quickly. He assured me that I no longer needed to feel guilty about missing church while I was washing "the calloused feet of a bent and wrinkled old woman . . . in a room where nobody saw and nobody knew."

Mom's care was my Christian service, and I was at peace with that answer. I was happy again, and it was vital for me to be in a happy mood because Mom always sensed my feelings. I couldn't hide anything from her. Since she reacted to my moods and my feelings, I had to be upbeat around her at all times. I talked to her kindly, and I treated her gently and with respect.

After Mom was placed at the nursing home, her personal hygiene became the responsibility of the nurses and nurse aides, and they actually did a much better job than I did. I never painted her fingernails with red or pink nail polish, but they often did. I never curled her hair because I just let it be natural. Sometimes, they put rollers in her hair to give it an extra style. I never fussed with makeup, yet they put blush on her cheeks and lipstick on her lips. The second drawer of Mom's nightstand had an ample supply of lotions, colognes, and cosmetics. With excellent personal hygiene, she always looked and smelled nice.

At Christmas time, they dressed Mom in her favorite red pantsuit. Nurse Mary told me that Mom looked just like Mrs. Santa Claus, and I smiled as I agreed with Mary's observation. Mom wore wire-framed glasses, her hair was pure white, and her cheeks looked red with blush. Her smile was so pleasant that her eyes danced when she smiled. Yes, she was a Mrs. Santa Claus when she wore her red pantsuit.

As we all know, women never outgrow the need to feel pretty. The philosophy at St. John Lutheran Home's is just that. The nurses, the nurse aides and the volunteers do all they can do to make their residents feel pretty with make-up and nail polish. Linda, one of Mom's nurse aides, said to me recently, "We like to groom them and to paint their fingernails. We do that for our residents if we have time. It makes them feel so pretty. And it gives us a good feeling when we see how pleased they are to feel pretty."

Whenever someone asks me about the kind of care my mother received at St. John Lutheran Home, I respond by saying, "Pink nail polish says it all." Of course, they look surprised at such an answer because they don't know what I mean. Then, I tell them that the nurse aides and the volunteers took time to help Mom feel pretty by putting on her make-up and by painting her nails a bright color.

Of course, I always emphasize the fact that they never gave up on Mom. When Alzheimer's brought her to the lowest of low in her second childhood, they could have said, "Why fuss with her face? She doesn't need make-up now. Why do her nails? She doesn't know the difference." Instead, they kept on treating her with dignity when all of her personal dignity was gone. They put blush on her cheeks, lipstick on her lips and nail polish on her fingers.

In fact, when I held my mother in my arms, that unforgettable Sunday afternoon when she was dying, I couldn't help but notice she had nail polish on her fingernails.

Pink nail polish.

Learning Detachment
Chapter Thirteen

November 1, 1995 . . . three months after Mom went to St. John.

It was one of those crisp, cool, fall days on the prairie and thankfully my sod house duties were finished for the season. I hung a sign on the deck of our house that read, "Let It Snow, Closed for the Season." Just for the fun of it, I took a walk on our prairie with Katie, our black Lab. The geese were flying over us as they headed south for the winter, and the smoky scent of burning leaves was in the air.

Suddenly, a feeling of deep sadness swept over me as I thought of Mom because I missed her every day. I missed her as my friend as well as my mother. How I wished she could be with me to enjoy the perfect fall day. Thoughts of her at the nursing home dampened my carefree mood. Emotionally, I had not learned how to let go of her.

Katie was sniffing in the grass and her tail was wagging rapidly because she was obviously on to something. Just then, four pheasants flew up from the prairie grass; she was flushing them out like Labs do. The birds sailed far into the prairie, too far for Katie to chase them.

At first, I thought that I had to be at the nursing home every day, and I stayed with Mom a long time to help pass the time for her. When I wasn't at the nursing home, she was on my mind constantly, and I felt guilty if I didn't spend lots of time with her. Finally, I realized that time was of no essence to her. She was in her own world, and she would not remember if I was there every day to see her or if I missed a few days. She was safe, she was occupied, and she was happy. It was time for me to move on with my life. I was free now to take time for myself and for my family. I was free, but she was always on my mind, and thoughts of her quite often dampened my spirits. Emotionally, I was still hanging on to her.

November 1, 1996 . . . a year later.

It was a beautiful fall day on the prairie, and I was putting things away for the winter. The sod house season was finally over, and now I could spend more time with Mom at the nursing home. For almost a year, I had carried a lot of guilt with me every time I visited her. I was afraid that at some point she would look at me and say, "Why did you put me here?" She never did that. In fact, one day my son Tom asked her this question, "Grandma, do you like living here?" Mom answered Tom with a "Yes." Then I was relieved, and gradually I worked through my guilty feelings. I was able to move forward without having to think of Mom every moment of the day. I was discovering detachment.

November 1, 1997 . . . two years later.

It was another fall day on the prairie, and my husband was helping me put away the sod cutter and the walking plow. Together we carried the park bench to the sod house. Every sign was pulled up and put away because it was time to burn the tall prairie grass. Prairie burns were a necessary part of taking care of our prairie exhibit. That evening, as I hung my sign on the deck, "Let It Snow, Closed for the Season," there was a hint of smoke in the air from the smoldering ashes of the prairie. Hanging out the sign always marked a milestone for me.

The tourist season had been a busy one for me. I tried to balance my thoughts of Mom and my daily concerns. Since I was constantly busy with guests and daily visitors, it was diffi-cult to schedule time to visit with Mom. When I did visit her, I made it a long visit. I pushed her in her wheelchair to all parts of St. John Lutheran Home. If it was nice, I took her outside to enjoy the courtyard. If it wasn't nice weather, we sat together in a lounge area where we could see the courtyard below us. Eventually, I learned that short visits worked well, too. Since she was only eight miles away, I could stop in for five minutes and see her any time I was in town.

Learning detachment meant learning a healthy balance between my life and Mom's life. If I couldn't be there for a week or so, I didn't feel horribly guilty about it. Frequently, I picked up the phone and dialed her station and I chatted for a few minutes with Heidi at the desk or with the nurses to find out the latest details of Mom's condition. Letting go comes in stages. I was doing better with learning detachment.

November 1, 1998 . . . three years later.

It was a crisp and cool fall day, and I was sitting on the park bench in the middle of our prairie. Everything else was put away for the season, except the bench that we had for weary visitors. Our dog Katie was sniffing her way through the prairie grasses looking for field mice or rabbits. When she found a nest, her tail wagged briskly. As usual, the geese were flying above me, heading south for the winter. Mom always enjoyed watching the geese. I wished she could be with me to spend these moments together. I felt sad to think about her deteriorating condition.

Katie came over to me and sat by me, and she looked at me with her chocolate brown eyes as if to say, "Come on, let's run in the prairie." It was a beautiful fall day, perfect for being spontaneous with a prairie run with Katie. The smell of distant smoke was in the air because a farmer had burnt his road ditches. "Come on Katie, let's do it." So Katie and I ran through the prairie grass. It was good to be alive and to be feeling well. Then I felt sad again. Mom loved to run just like I did now. She was in a geri chair; her walking days were over. My spirits were dampened again. I could do everything, sit, stand, walk, and run. She couldn't do any of these anymore. I felt guilty about having fun when she was suffering.

I sat on the park bench again and pondered these things. Now that she was at St. John Home, I was free to do my work, and I was free to enjoy my family, but sad thoughts of her kept me from enjoying the times that I should be enjoying. She was suffering, and I couldn't let go of the thought of it. Her suffering often dampened my spirits. There was more to learn about this process called detachment.

The color of the sky was changing, and I watched the sun slowly drop to the horizon. Mom loved to watch the sunsets. I missed watching sunsets with her. She always stopped whatever she was doing and watched the sky change its colors. Quite often she would say to me, "No artist could paint the colors of the sky tonight. No artist could capture those colors on canvas. No one but God could paint that sunset."

The prairie looked different at dusk. I pulled my coat around me because it was getting chilly. Katie and I walked back to the house together in a somber mood. I had to hang out the sign, "Let It Snow, Closed for the Season."

November 1, 1999 . . . four years later.

It was a cold snowy day on the prairie unlike those perfect fall days of other years. With my winter coat around me, I was walking along the trails to check all parts of the exhibit making sure it was winterized. Katie was walking with me, a little slower this year because her age was catching up with her. Geese were flying south again. Mom always loved to hear the geese as they flew in the sky honking as they went.

Losing someone to Alzheimer's is like losing someone twice. I was grieving while the Mother that I once knew was slowly fading away from me. At the same time, I was preparing myself for her death. Yet, I was trying to stay connected to her, and at the same time, I was working on detachment. It was a dilemma for me. "How could I learn to enjoy myself while I was grieving for her? How could I enjoy anything without feeling guilty about it?"

Mom helped me with this dilemma. Well, not actually. It was her words of advice that helped me. On my wedding day, as I was leaving for my honeymoon, Mom hugged me and said, " You're married now. I'm so happy for you. Have a good life together!" Mom wanted me to be happy and to enjoy my life. All mothers want that for their daughters. She said it often, "Have a good time."

So, I thought about those words. If she could have talked to me then, and she couldn't, she would have said something like this, "Virginia, don't let my condition spoil things for you. Have a good time anyway!"

Admittedly, if the shoe were on the other foot and if I were in the nursing home, I would have encouraged my mom to go on with her life and to enjoy it. I would have told her to have a good time.

After that day, I worked at thinking positive thoughts. Some sad thoughts were bound to come my way at times, but it was better to not dwell on sad thoughts. It was better to let them go. Why let them ruin a perfectly happy time? Mom wanted me to be happy. Gradually, I learned how to have a good time. And amazingly, I learned how to enjoy the ordinary times. I learned to seize the moment and make my own fun. I found that I could be spontaneous with my fun, like running through the prairie grass with my dog Katie.

Brrrr.....that afternoon the prairie was cold, so I pulled my coat around me, and I decided that I needed a brisk prairie walk to warm me. "Come on Katie, let's do it." So, Katie and I walked the prairie trails that afternoon. We saw geese flying above us even though it was snowing that afternoon. There was a lesson for me to learn from the geese. I needed to be like them, to rise above my circumstances. I couldn't change my circumstances, but I could change how I viewed them. I needed to think positive thoughts to rise above it all. Be happy! Enjoy life! That was Mom's wish for me!

When Katie and I walked back to our house, it was time to put out the sign. "Let it Snow, Closed for the Season." I smiled as I hung out the sign on that November day, because instead of leaves falling in my front yard, snow was falling. We already had two inches on the ground.

Mom Waves Good-bye
Chapter Fourteen

Several times in my life, I have experienced anesthesia and the process that it takes to awaken from it. In the recovery room, awareness comes slowly for me in surges, brief moments at first and then longer periods of clarity until the fogginess clears completely. At totally unpredictable times, Alzheimer's people have the ability to think clearly. For some reason the brain has a surge of energy, the transmitters make the right connection, and the fogginess clears. To be with the person when it happens and to share in the time of awareness is a miracle. God arranged some times of clarity with Mom as she told us good-bye. For me it happened almost four years before Mom died. For my brother it was much later, less than a year before she died.

Mom's roommate, Laura, died in May of 1996. She was a sweet little lady that reminded me of my grandma Bausch, my dad's mother. In fact, Mom thought that she was her grandma Pitman, and she actually called her Grandma. Every night they spent together as roommates, Mom went to sleep with the comfort of thinking her grandma was there with her. As busy as I was on that May evening, I took time to drive to the Sturm Funeral Home for Laura's visitation. Later, as I pulled out of the funeral home's parking lot, I stopped at the stop sign and paused for a few minutes pondering what to do next. Maybe I should turn left and visit Mom, or maybe I should turn right and head for home. I felt a strong urge to visit Mom.

Since I hadn't called the charge nurse ahead of time to say that I was coming in late for a visit, Mom was already in bed when I got there. I walked to her room at the end of the hall-way and peaked in the door that was slightly ajar. She was sleeping. I hesitated being there because I hated to wake up Mom if she was sleeping. I turned away and walked down the hallway. Sara met me at the nurse's station. "You came to see your mom, didn't you? Is she sleeping?" I nodded to Sara that she was. "Virginia, don't go. Walk with me to her room. I have to give her some medication."

"I really should go home, Sara. I was in town for Laura's visitation. I don't need to stay. I can stop some other time."

Again, I felt that inward urge to stay. So I walked with Sara to Mom's room. I waited at the end of the hallway until Sara came out of Mom's room. "Go ahead, Virginia. She's awake now."

Mom's room looked different now that Laura was gone. It was empty and bare on one side. I gave Mom a hug, and I sank in a chair beside her. "Grandma's real sick tonight," said Mom. Obviously, Mom didn't realize that Laura had died, and I didn't want to tell her about it.

For a long time Mom rambled on and on about things that made no sense to me. Several times she reminded me that Grandma was real sick. Since it was impossible to carry on a conversation with Mom, I just let her ramble. Eventually, I got up from the chair, and I walked around the room for a while because I was feeling sleepy. Then I sat in a different chair, one that was at the foot of Mom's bed. "Grandma's real sick tonight. Where's Grandma?" Mom stopped talking for a while. I didn't want to tell her about Laura. I hoped that she wouldn't notice the emptiness of the room.

Then it happened. Clarity. She looked at me, really looked at me with a cognitive, intelligent look. Her eyes and her face looked brighter as she stared at my face for a while before saying, "Why, Virginia. It's you! It's been so long." Suddenly, she woke up from the fogginess of her mind, and she finally saw me clearly. It was a miracle that I was there to experience it with her. I almost went home. We were alone in Mom's room because Laura was gone. It was perfectly planned for us.

Mom had called me by my name, Virginia. I hadn't heard

her say my name for a year, since that memorable night I crawled across the living room floor to hear her whisper it in prayer. For ten minutes, she was the Mom that I knew before Alzheimer's confused her. I shared details about my husband and our five children while she listened intently. Then she asked about Russell, Anne and their three children. As I talked about them, she was delighted in hearing what each one was doing. Then she told me how much she appreciated everything they did for her. Oh, I wished Russell were here in the room with us right now.

As I told her everything she wanted to know, her brown eyes danced when she listened to every detail, and she smiled that great smile of hers. Then she told me that she appreciated me taking care of her, and she motioned for me to come over to her so she could hug me. I got up from my chair, I went to her, and we hugged each other as she thanked me again for everything.

And then she was gone.

Clarity was gone as quickly as it came to her. I could tell by the expression on her face. She didn't focus on me like she had been. Fogginess returned. Then she said, "Grandma's real sick tonight."

As Mom returned to her senseless rambling, I sat for a while in the chair next to her. Her clarity was an eerie experience, and my mind had to digest it. I had forgotten what she was like because it had been so long since Mom and I had visited with each other. In a few minutes before my very eyes, she transformed into my mother again. It was uncanny. And to think I could have missed it because I had debated whether or not I should visit Mom that evening. When I found her asleep, I nearly went home, but something inside me urged me to stay. Later, I recognized it as a special time that God had planned for me.

Finally, Mom's rambling stopped, and she was dozing in her bed, so I gave her a gentle hug and told her that I loved her and left her room. I saw nurse Sara in the hallway, and I told her about Mom's time of clarity. "That happens some-times, Virginia. Good! I'm glad you stayed for her. That's a special moment for you two. And you had the room all to yourselves. I think it was planned."

"Thanks Sara for encouraging me to stay tonight. I would have missed that wonderful moment with Mom if I had gone home."

As I was driving home, I played the scene over and over in my mind. Mom said to me, "Virginia, it's you. It's been so long." She was right; it had been a long time since we really connected, a terribly long time. The whole thing was amazing as I thought about it. I wondered if there would be another time like it. Probably not. As I drove along, tears came rolling down my cheeks because somehow I knew Mom had just waved good-bye to me.

Three years later, my brother Russell experienced a slight moment of awareness when he was visiting Mom. At that time, she was well into her second childhood. The moment of clarity was brief because Mother's condition was like that of an infant. She was napping in her bed when Russell and Anne arrived that day after driving four hours from Nebraska. Nurse Mary awakened her and arranged her bed so she could see them. Russell pulled a chair up to her bed and sat close to her. He held her frail hands in his, while he told her all about his family, his farming and his work. For a half an hour or so, Russell talked to her just like he had always talked to her knowing that she would not be able to say anything to him.

Then it came. The moment of clarity!

Mom was looking downward at the hands that were hold-ing hers. Then she looked up at his face and she said, "Oh . . . it's you . . . Russell." And they connected for just a moment as they held hands. Then she looked at her daughter-in-law standing behind Russell and she said, "Anne." Again, she looked down at the hands that were holding hers. When she looked up again, awareness was gone.

For a brief moment, she waved good-bye to them.

The clarity lasted only a moment, but what a moment it was for Russell. His mother had spoken his name because she momentarily recognized him. He was so overcome with emotion that he left the room to find a quiet place where he could be alone. She had waved good-bye, and he knew it.

When Russell left the room, Anne sat in the chair and held Mom's hand as she cried softly. Mom had also spoken her name because she had recognized her. It was her good-bye. And she knew it.

Moments of clarity. Perfectly timed. Perfectly planned. Priceless moments for the family.

Good-byes are always sad times for loved ones, and so are their last words. Mom's last audible words to me were spoken a month before she died. For her to say anything cognitive was a sheer moment of clarity. My husband and I stopped to see her that Sunday morning as we were returning from church. Whenever I came to Mother, I hugged her, and I told her at least three or four times, "Mom I'm here now. I love you, " because I wanted to make sure she understood the meaning of those words.

One of Mom's nurse aides, Jill, came to where we were seated at the dining room table and she bent down to Mom, and said slowly and clearly, "Ethel, your daughter is here now. Virginia is here." She repeated it for Mom. "Ethel, Virginia is here now."

Surprisingly Mom said, "I know that." Mom spoke very slowly in a voice that was weak and low. Jill was near to her, and she repeated each word as Mom said it.

"I . . . know . . . that." Mom was telling us that she knew I was there. I had just hugged her and told her that I loved her. Now Mom was assuring me she knew I was with her. We were experiencing a wonderful love connection.

Then she said something else in a mumbled voice. It was difficult for us to understand, but Jill got closer to Mom, and she translated Mom's last words for us.

"It's been so long."

Valley of the Shadow
Chapter Fifteen

Mom's Alzheimer's had taken us on a journey that had lasted for twenty years. In her moments of clarity, Mom had waved good-bye to us. Now it was time to bring the journey to a close, but we couldn't because it was not in our hands to do so. It was in God's hands, and we had to wait for God's timing. Because we were human, we wanted to know exactly when that would be, so our whole family began to think and to pray, "How much longer, Lord? When Lord?" If indeed Mom's last words were what Jill thought she had said on that Sunday morning, "It's been so long," Mom was also feeling like it was time for the journey to end.

In mid-October I noticed a definite decline in Mom's condition. When Chaplain Mary and I visited about the decline, she gave me a book to read about the dying process. I recognized some of the early signs of dying.

In November, Nurse Mary said we could ask for hospice to help Mom with her final days. I was surprised to know that hospice helps in nursing homes because I thought their help was limited to at-home situations. Mary filled out the required paper work, but after Thanksgiving, Mary was notified that Hospice could not honor her request to come for Mom.

Hospice declined because Mom's medical chart did not indicate she was dying that soon, meaning the medical chart had to show that Mom would die within six months. True, Mom's chart showed a rather healthy woman yet. With Alzheimer's it is very difficult to separate the early signs of dying from the person's Alzheimer's condition. Nevertheless, I had a strong feeling that Mom was dying, and I went by that feeling. In November, I cleared my schedule so that I could spend as much time as I could at her side. I have no regrets. Mom died three months later. I was her hospice.

At Christmas time, the flu hit her station, and six of the residents died from its complications. Many of her caregivers, nurses and nurse aides, were ill with the flu, but Mom was spared. Amazingly, Mom not only missed the flu, but she also lived long enough to greet the year 2000, the new millennium.

As January passed slowly, Mom was terribly weak. Actually, I expected that at some point, I would get a call from St. John saying that Mom had quietly slipped away in the night. But that didn't happen. February came instead, and Mom was still with us.

We lived one day at a time. Mom's condition was always our concern.

Finally, something remarkable happened on the first Sunday of February while we were in church. The morning church service featured the youth group as the worship team. A young girl from the worship team stepped forward and took the microphone in her hand and sang a new song. She returned the microphone to the stand and for some reason she quoted the fourth verse from the twenty-third Psalm (KJV). "Yea, though I walk through the valley of the shadow of death, I will fear no evil: for thou art with me; thy rod and thy staff they comfort me." Then she looked up to the balcony where we were sitting that day, as if to say to us, "This verse is for you." Right then, I knew Mom's time had come.

I knew we were heading into the valley of the shadow of death. As we drove home that day, I had comforting thoughts that seemed like a heavenly e-mail, one that echoed the message of the twenty-third Psalm. "Your mother's death is near. Now listen to me. Don't be afraid. I will be with you. The valley of the shadow of death is only a shadow. Remember, I conquered death when I died on the cross. Don't be afraid. I will go with you."

When we were at home again, I pressed the flashing button of my telephone message machine, and it was nurse Sara saying that Mom's condition had worsened, and that I should check with them. She assured me it was not an emergency, but it was important that I come to the nursing home as soon as possible. So I hurried to make a quick Sunday dinner for my family.

While I was clearing the table and stacking the dishes in the dishwasher, I thought about Mom's decline. She was a whisper of the woman that she used to be, so frail and thin. Her days were spent in a geri chair in the reclined position. Her arms were usually at her side with her hands unable to clasp anything. Her mouth was always open as she breathed heavily. Her face fluctuated from an anxious look to a blank stare.

I couldn't help but think about her approaching death. How will I handle it? Which day of the week will it happen? Will it be in the middle of the night? Will I be there for her when it happens? Will I be calm and strong? My mind had so many questions.

As soon as I was able, I drove to the nursing home thinking about Mom's condition. Was it the flu? Did she have pneumonia? Was her heart finally getting weak? Or was it her swallowing problem? Nurse Mary had recently called for the help of a throat therapist to help Mom with her swallowing.

When I arrived at the nurse's station, nurse Sara talked to me about Mom's condition. In spite of all their efforts, she was losing her reflex to swallow. She was running a slight temperature, probably a bladder infection. The staff was keeping her comfortable, and they were treating her for the infection. At this point there were several reasons for concern so they were keeping a close watch over her.

I understood how serious the situation was when nurse Vicki came to Mom's room with a tray of food at suppertime. Vicki spent a long time trying to get Mom to eat. She put one spoonful in her mouth, and she talked Mom into swallowing it by saying over and over, "Ethel, swallow this. Swallow it,

Ethel. You can do it, Ethel. Swallow please. Just swallow it."
After saying that several times, Mom finally swallowed the
spoonful. Vicki told Mom, "Good girl, Ethel." Vicki put
another spoonful into Mom's mouth, and she gently massaged
her throat as she coaxed her to swallow again. The process
went on for a lengthy time until Vicki was satisfied that Mom
had taken a few spoonfuls of nourishment. I knew things were
very serious.

When Dr. Schmitz met with me on Tuesday, he explained
to me that Mom's brain was no longer making the reflex that
told her to swallow. In fact, Mom could no longer swallow
anything, not even her own saliva. I knew what our options
were at this point. We could request a feeding tube for Mom,
or we could let her die naturally. My brother and I had discussed these options beforehand, and we were in agreement
with no feeding tube. Mom would not want to linger any
longer; we were more than ready to let her go.

When it was time to tell Dr. Schmitz our decision, I wondered what he would say to me, and I also wondered what the
staff would think of such a decision. Finally, I told Dr.
Schmitz that my brother and I were firm in our decision to
not have a feeding tube for Mom. I looked at his face to see
his reaction to my words. I saw a smile as he said, "Virginia,
that is the natural way to die. We will do our best to keep your
mother comfortable."

Thankfully, the nurses and the nurse aides were also supportive of our decision. When I expressed my desire to do a
vigil for Mom, nurse Mary ordered a soft recliner from the
lounge to be brought to Mom's room and placed beside her
bed. Mary ordered meals from the kitchen and brought them
to me on a tray. Each morning at dawn, I drove home to shower and change clothes, and then I returned to my mom's side.

Mom's comfort was our concern, especially the dryness of
her mouth because she was breathing with her mouth open.
Mary gave me a spray bottle of water, and she carefully showed
me how to spray Mom's mouth with just enough mist to

moisten it, but not too much that would cause her to choke.
Since Mom no longer swallowed, too much mist would be a
problem for her to handle. It was hard to see Mom in this condition. In a small way, it helped me to know that I was doing
something for her. When I sprayed her mouth, she brought
her lips together and let the mist refresh her. I imagined her
saying to me, "Mmm . . . that feels so good."

To comfort and refresh her soul, I brought a CD player to
her bedside, and I played instrumental hymn music around
the clock for her. All day and all night until the vigil was over,
she heard hymn music, especially her favorite songs, "Jesus
Loves Me.," "Rock of Ages," "What a Friend We Have In
Jesus," "His Eye Is On The Sparrow," " How Great Thou
Art," and "Amazing Grace." Mom was a still a person within the shell of her body, and her spirit was being refreshed by
the music.

Even though Mom seemed unresponsive, nurse Mary
assured me that she could hear everything. The nurse aides
spoke gently to her, always calling her by her name. Her condition was not discussed in front of her, and only positive
things were said. Nurses Mary and Sara urged my brother and
I to speak openly to Mom and to tell her what we needed to
say. They encouraged us to hold her gently and to hug her
often. She would feel and know our presence and our love.

Her nurse aides changed her diaper and repositioned her
often to prevent bedsores. Special booties were placed on her
feet to relieve the pressure on her heels. Tylenol suppositories
were given to her for pain and discomfort.

On Friday of that long week, Russell and Anne came to
join me in the vigil. I felt an oasis of refreshment when they
came to be with me for the vigil. We took turns sitting in the
recliner by Mom's bedside. We were glad to know that she
could still hear our voices, so we hugged her, we held her, and
we told her we loved her. She was the best Mom ever.

Chaplain Mary from St. John Lutheran Home kept in
close touch with me. In private, we talked openly about

Mom's approaching death. I expressed my wish to be there when Mom's final breath came. She cautioned me in this by saying to me, "People often die in the same manner they live. Some die privately because they are basically private people. Some die openly with a room full of relatives. Some wait until their closest relatives leave the room, and they die alone, sparing them of the pain of saying good-bye."

I was surprised to learn that a dying person can sometimes control the timing of death. So I said, "Mary, I want to be there for Mom when it happens. I hope that Mom will allow me that." I knew that Mom was a private person, and I knew that she would not want a whole room of people beside her at the final moments. Since Mom and I were close, I wanted to be there for her, but if she slipped away from me without me being there, I would excuse her for doing that.

"Virginia, you could pray about it. You could ask God for that wish. He may or He may not grant that to you." Then Chaplain Mary and I prayed aloud together about my wish to be there for Mom. After we prayed together, I had peace about it.

When I needed a break from my vigil, I often walked across the hall to Grace's room. Since I couldn't speak to her directly because she had lost her hearing, I reached for her spiral notebook, and I wrote a cheery note to her with her pen. She eagerly read my message, and she smiled at me. Then her face got serious, and she spoke to me in a loud voice as her hand gestured in the direction of my mom's room. "How's your mom doing?" I answered by writing in her notebook these words, "She's the same." And Grace squeezed my hand in sympathy.

Other times, when I needed a break from sitting next to Mom, I visited with a tiny but energetic widow named Viola. She had a vibrant mind and a positive outlook. Parkinson's made her head nod and her hands shake, but she had a warm and lovely smile that radiated her personality.

Other times, I simply walked the hallways trying to stay upbeat about my situation. On one of these walks, I recalled that Chaplain Mary had spoken of another woman in the nursing home who was dying. I felt like I wanted to connect with the relatives of that woman to see how they were doing. I walked to another area of the nursing home to look for the room of the dying woman. I found the room with the sign on the doorpost, "Oxygen In Use." The door was closed.

A nurse told me that the dying woman was a widow with no children. I knew the staff was doing everything to comfort her, but I was sad for her because she had no husband, no children, and no grandchildren to be with her as she was dying. When I walked by her room again, the door was open, and I saw that she had a visitor in a wheelchair that was parked close to her bed.

Surprisingly, my little Parkinson's friend Viola had come to sit with the dying woman, and she was holding her hand. Soft hymn music was playing, just as it was in Mom's room. Besides the fact that they were both childless widows, I wondered what else was motivating Viola to care so deeply for the dying one. Quietly, I walked into the room, and I put my hand gently on Viola's shoulder.

Viola turned to me a bit surprised as she felt my hand on her shoulder. Her head was nodding; her eyes were swollen with sorrow; her voice was trembling, and her words were very slow. "This is Leora. She is my sister." Instantly, my hand went to my mouth to cover a tiny gasp of surprise. Now I recognized the woman in the bed as the constant companion of Viola, but I hadn't realized it was her sister. So I gave Viola a sympathetic hug, and I quietly left the room.

As I walked the hallway again, I marveled at what I had just seen, a ninety-eight year-old woman sitting by the bedside of her ninety-six-year-old sister. Then, I felt like God was speaking to me when I had these thoughts, "Leora is dying now, and she has her older sister at her side. I saved Viola for this time. I planned it that way. When it's Viola's turn to die, I have a plan for her, too. And I have a plan for your mother. Keep trusting Me."

When you sit by a loved one who is dying, it's like being in a cocoon. Time stands still. When death is over, you fly back to the real world and deal with the ordinary details of life. For a week, I was in the cocoon. Once in a while I saw glimpses of the real world. The big screen TV in the lounge was on the sports channel, and the reporter was in Florida interviewing a race driver about the upcoming Daytona 500. When I picked up the Advance Press newspaper, it was full of ads for Valentine's Day. The cleaning ladies were talking about the ten-below-zero temperature, as they were moving a bed into a room that had been waxed and shined.

Each time I took a break from Mom's side, I had to give myself a pep talk before I returned to Mom's room because of her appearance as she was dying. The first look at Mom and the first five minutes at her side were the hardest to do. After conquering the first five minutes, I could sit with her for hours. When I walked into the room, I had to brace myself for the first look, and then I sat in the recliner for a while and prayed for the strength to do what I needed to do. Then I spoke gently to her as I hugged her, "Mom, I'm here now. I love you." Strength always came to me as I reached for her water bottle and sprayed her mouth with mist. Her lips came together, and I imagined her voice saying to me, "That feels so good."

One of the high school aides walked by my mother's room one afternoon as I was sitting in the recliner praying for strength to look at Mom in that condition. When Dustin saw me brush away a tear, he turned around and came back to the room. Then he stepped inside and asked me, "Are you going to be all right?" Then he walked over to where I was sitting, gave me a hug and left the room.

That amazing, heart-felt hug from a seventeen-year-old recharged me.

Whenever the nurses checked Mom, they pulled back her blankets and looked at the coloring of her feet. Seeing purple blotches would mean mottling, a sign that her circulation was shutting down. Then death would be near. My son's wife Heidi is a nurse, and she told me to also check Mom's knees for signs of mottling. Sometimes it shows on the knees before it shows on the feet. Saturday was the sixth day of being in the valley of the shadow of death, and I was getting weary. Finally, I asked nurse Mary, "How much longer can this take?"

"Death is different for everyone. It could be awhile yet. I just don't know. We don't see mottling yet. It's hard to say when."

When I asked God the same question, He gave me His usual answer, "In my time, Virginia. In my time."

The Purple Tide
Chapter Sixteen

When I was a child, on hot summer days, the neighbor kids and I went to a sandy beach to swim and to play. Sometimes we made sand castles. Sometimes we buried each other with sand. We took turns lying on the warm beach, while we used plastic shovels and pails full of sand to cover each other. Then we carried pails of water from the lake to the person buried in a heavy layer of sand. We poured water on the person starting at the feet first, then the legs, then the knees, then the waist, and then the chest. We intended to make the person feel the sensation of a tide. Finally someone would say, "Let's not play this any more. Let's go for a swim in the lake." So we uncovered the person and helped him rise up from the sandy burial, and together we ran into the water for a swim. The game was over.

At the dawn of Sunday morning, after a long and restless night by Mom's side, I was ready to go home to shower and be refreshed. I pulled back the covers and checked Mom's feet. They were pale but warm. I remembered Heidi's words for me to check Mom's knees, too. A purple blotch about the size of a fifty-cent piece was very noticeable on each of her knees. Mottling had begun.

It was Sunday, the seventh day in the valley of the shadow, and I remembered the words from the twenty-third Psalm, as the young girl at church quoted them the previous Sunday morning, "Yea, though I walk through the valley of the shadow of death, I will fear no evil: for thou art with me; thy rod and thy staff they comfort me." It had been a long week. God had been with us just as He had promised. Now, perhaps our walk though the valley of the shadow of death was coming to an end.

At around seven o'clock, I left Mom's room and drove home. I told my family about the purple knee blotches, a sign that the mottling process had begun. They understood Mom's need for privacy at this time. They also understood that at some point I would need their support. My husband and my sons would be joining me whenever I gave them a call.

On my return to the nursing home, I stopped to buy some sweet rolls as a treat for the staff to eat at break time. When I walked into the grocery store, I was delighted to see that they were selling fresh flowers for Valentine's Day, and I bought Mom a bouquet of red and white tulips. When I arrived at Mom's room, one of the aide's put them in a vase, and we set them on her nightstand next to her bed. Hymn music was playing softly for her. I gave her a gentle hug, and I stroked her hair and caressed her face. "Mom, I am here now. I love you."

When nurse Mary came into the room, she gently pulled back the bed covers to check her feet. They were bluish purple. Almost two hours had passed since I first noticed the blotches on her knees. "How long does the mottling take?" I asked her.

"It's different for every individual. Your mom has a strong heart. She's what I call pioneer stock. It could take hours; it could take until tomorrow. We have no way of knowing how long it will be. We'll do our best to keep her comfortable. If she needs oxygen, we can do that for her. We'll see how it goes for her."

I wished that it would happen that day because the waiting was hard. Her breathing rattled inside her chest, and it had an irregular pattern, a rather scary one. She stopped breathing for a while, there was a long pause, and then she started breathing again. Waiting for death was like waiting for birth to happen; it was a strange similarity. No one knows the precise moment, only God knows.

When I phoned my brother in Nebraska to tell him about the purple tide, I advised him to stay home because I sensed that he wouldn't make it in time. I also told him that I could handle it better if I didn't have to worry about him driving fast in snowy February weather. We both agreed that it was good that he had been with us the previous day.

By ten o'clock, the purple tide had reached her knees, leaving her legs and her feet blue and cold to our touch. Her eyes were glassy now. They were open but she didn't react to the spray bottle when I brought it close to her face.

By noon, the purple tide had reached her chest. Then I called my husband and my sons to be with me. My sons had a quiet moment with their grandmother as they told her good-bye. At one o'clock, I sent my sons home. My husband stayed by my side.

At one thirty, the purple tide was up to her neck. She was breathing on her own so there was no need for oxygen. Mom's aides repositioned her often, gently calling her name as they lifted her frail and bluish body. At one forty-five, she gasped a deep long gasp when they were repositioning her limp body. Then nurse Mary told us it would be soon.

My husband was by my side, and I was holding Mom in my arms. Her face felt warm and it had some color, but the rest of her was a cold bluish purple. I talked to her constantly as I held her. "We love you, Mom. Thank you for being our Mom. You were the best Mom that anyone could ever have. It's okay to leave us now, Mom."

Shortly after two o'clock, my husband and I witnessed an amazing thing. Her appearance changed as she experienced a burst of energy. Mom's lips silently moved as if she were talking to someone in the room, someone we could not see with our eyes. Her heavenly escort had arrived to usher her to the other side of death. Then she smiled. After smiling, she closed her eyes.

Her breathing became shallow and in slow motion, like a fish out of the water. Slowly . . . very faintly . . . she breathed tiny . . . shallow breaths . . . until she stopped. It was 2:10 and she was gone.

A Smile For Her Escort
Chapter Seventeen

As the purple tide was rising that unforgettable day, so were my emotions. Because of Mom's erratic breathing pattern, as it stopped, paused, and started again, my anxiety was escalating. The tension was building, then it was falling, and then it was rising again like an inward performance of Handel's Messiah. When the purple tide reached her neck, my heart was pounding to the rising drama of the situation. My nervousness was much like the rhythm of the Halleluiah's of that famous Halleluiah Chorus.

The final Halleluiah was my emotional highpoint, the moment she smiled at her escort and then closed her eyes. It was an unforgettable moment of moments! For a few minutes longer, she continued breathing in slow motion with tiny shallow breaths until she ultimately stopped. I was holding her in my arms when her warmth slowly disappeared. Finally, I let go of her, and I stood away from her bed as if to give a standing ovation for what I had just experienced. With my eyes lifted upward, I said aloud, "Thank you God! She's free now! She's Yours!"

It took years for the sands of Alzheimer's to trap my mom, like the heavy wet sand that almost buried us at the beach. It took hours for the purple tide to slowly ascend her body. When it reached her neck, it was far enough. It was time for her escort to say to her, "You don't have to be here anymore. Shake off the sands of time. You're free now. Come with me into eternity."

To be released from her body must have been a wonderful sensation for her. Her soul and her spirit had been trapped inside that crusty shell for a long time. What a glorious moment when she was set free. I couldn't help but wonder what it was like for her. Was her release at the precise time when she smiled at her escort and closed her eyes? Or did it happen minutes later when she breathed her last shallow breath? Since there are no answers, I can only wonder. Did her spirit leave immediately or did it linger before it passed to the other side? Again, I can only wonder.

Who was the heavenly escort? Was it an angel? Was it Jesus? Was it someone familiar to her, who had gone before her? Perhaps her mother? Perhaps her father?

Her lips were silently moving as she was calling out to her heavenly escort, and she smiled a wonderful smile. Was it her husband? Or perhaps her sister? I can only wonder.

For seven hours Mom's body labored to free her spirit. How did she feel the moment her spirit was released? When she joined her escort, was it like the triumph of finishing a long and rugged climb to the mountain peak? If so, did she linger to enjoy the victory of her triumph? Did she view the world below her and the heavens above her before she disappeared into eternity? I can only wonder.

Perhaps the departure from her body was a rapid one, like being launched in a rocket. If so, did she see the sun, moon and stars around her as she spiraled her way into eternity? Maybe her release was not that dramatic, maybe it was more like the sensation of abruptly letting go, like when a skydiver decides to jump from the airplane into the open sky? Perhaps she lingered awhile as she floated her way into eternity. I can only wonder.

Or perhaps her spirit was released with extreme quietness and serenity as when an orchid slowly opens its bloom? Or when the sun slowly sinks in the west?

I can only wonder.

My Final Walk With Mom
Chapter Eighteen

Mom and I took many walks together in my lifetime. She walked the floor with me when I was born a premature baby. Together we walked through childhood. She walked me to my first day of school. She was there for my high school graduation and for my college graduation. We walked and shopped for that special dress for her to wear at my wedding. She walked the floor with my baby daughter. We walked together through many years and many memories.

Now it was time to have our last walk together. It was time to remove Mom's body from her room. Nurse Mary notified Sturm Funeral Home in Springfield while I waited by the nurse's station. I couldn't help but wonder who would come to perform this service for us. Would it be a man or would it be a woman? As I watched the hallway toward the elevator, I finally saw a woman dressed in black coming toward me pushing a cart. She was young, attractive and friendly, and she pleasantly introduced herself as Stephanie. I noticed she had snowflakes on her long black wool coat.

As she slowly pushed the cart to Mom's room, I walked to the nearest window to look outside. It was snowing huge fluffy snowflakes in the courtyard where Mom and I used to walk on summer days. The bench where Mom and I sat for hours and drank in the sunshine was now covered with snow. The fountain that sprayed water in the sunlight, making thousands of prisms for us to enjoy, was cold and still. I watched a cardinal come to the bird feeder just below the window and feast on the sunflower seeds and then fly away.

When I turned from the window, I saw the woman in black coming down the hallway with the cart that had Mom's body in a body bag. I went to her and told her that I wanted to walk with my mom. She smiled at me; she understood. Together we walked to the nurse's station. I fully expected us to take the back way, to the elevator and go to the basement level, then to the east parking lot behind the nursing home. Mom's body would be put into a black funeral hearse, and the woman in black would slowly drive away. But that's not how it happened.

With dignity, we went out the front entrance to her white minivan parked under the canopy. We took the route that I took every time I visited Mom. We walked past the nurse's station, past the dining area where Mom ate her meals, past the grandfather clock that was chiming three o'clock, and past the big screen TV that was showing an old western in black and white. Slowly, we made our way past rooms with the numbers 210, 208, 206, 204, 202 and 200. Some of the residents were napping, some were watching their TV's, and some were enjoying visits from relatives and friends.

When we came to the elevator, the woman in black pushed the button to open the door, and carefully we pushed the cart inside. The door closed, and she pushed the button for first floor. The ride was short, and the door soon opened for us. Slowly, we made our way past the Marie J. Arndt Community Room, where we held Mom's eighty-fifth birthday party. Slowly, we made our way past the conference room where we met for our care conferences, and past the Giving Tree, a bronze image of a tree mounted to the wall with hundreds of bronze leaves imprinted with the names of former residents whose families had given a donation in their memory.

As we made our way with dignity, we walked by Sunday visitors, old and young alike. When they saw us, they paused from their chatter and their laughter, and they stood in silence as they looked at us with respect.

Finally, we made our way to the front lobby and the front desk. The automatic doors sensed our presence and opened for us. Slowly, we pushed the cart through the doorway. Then we were outside at the front entrance of St. John Lutheran Home. The woman in black had come in a white van that she had parked under the canopy of the front entrance. Carefully, she put the body bag and the cart into the back of her van, and then we closed the doors.

Snowflakes were falling on us as we stood for a moment of silence. Then she said good-bye to me. She climbed into the driver's side of the van and slowly drove away. I watched the white van as it made its way down the long lane and turned to the right, gradually disappearing into the swirling February snow.

It was an honor to walk with my mom. It was our last walk together.

A Snowflake's Design
Chapter Nineteen

For a while, I stood under the canopy watching the snow falling softly in the distance. It had been a long day while I was waiting for Mom to die. Even though it had just happened, it seemed unreal to me. It was a relief to know that her suffering was over. She was with the Lord now. She was safe with Him.

Finally I decided to go inside again. It was time for me to return to Mom's room and take care of her things. While I was gone, the nurse aides had made her bed placing her doll on the bedspread propped against the pillow. Just an hour before that time, Mom was lying in her bed. I was glad her doll was there instead.

Nurse Mary helped me with the packing process. She opened Mom's closet and reached to the shelf where Mom's blue suitcase was sitting. I hadn't seen it for years. Then she handed me Mom's walking stick. It had been on the top shelf of Mom's closet for a long time. I looked at Mom's clothes, nothing fancy, but they served the purpose. I asked nurse Mary if she would give Mom's clothing to someone, and she promised she would do that for me. I kept Mom's summer jacket because I wanted to put it on once in a while and feel close to her again. I used Mom's suitcase to pack the rest of her things. There wasn't much to pack because my husband and my sons had already taken most of it.

The red and white tulips that I had given Mom were in a vase sitting on the nightstand next to her bed. I momentarily held them in my hands, and I thought about when I had bought them in the grocery store that morning. It seemed ages ago. Tulips are one of the first flowers that bloom in the spring. I took comfort in knowing that like always, winter would be followed by spring. Hopefully, the same would be true in my grief. Winter emotions would eventually be followed by spring ones.

Then this verse came to mind, "To every thing there is a season, and a time to every purpose under the heaven: A time to be born and a time to die; a time to plant, and a time to pluck up that which is planted." Ecclesiastes Chapter 3 verses 1-2 (KJV)

It was comforting to know that Mom's death was at God's appointed time. The scripture verse says there is a time for everything. Today it was the time for death. It was a long day. I remembered getting up at sunrise and looking at Mom's knees to see if there were any signs of mottling. That's when I saw the purple blotches. The mottling process took around seven hours. Actually, it seemed like an eternity.

As I packed Mom's Bible into her blue suitcase, I thought about the time when Chaplain Mary and I had prayed together asking God to grant me a special request. I wanted to be there for Mom when she died, and I was. As I thought about her final minutes, I knew that I had been granted more than just being there for her. I experienced her surge of energy. I saw her silently calling out to someone in the distance. I knew someone had come to be with her, to escort her to the other side. I saw her smile that wonderful smile.

While it was happening, I said aloud to my husband who was next to me. "Look, her lips are moving. She sees someone. She's calling out to someone. Look! She smiled. She's talking to someone." Her final moments were awesome. Yes, God granted far more than I had requested.

When everything was packed and it was time to leave Mom's room for the last time, I gave the bouquet of tulips to Mom's roommate, Marie, and I thanked her for being so good to Mom. Then I walked to the nurse's station and thanked Mary and Linda for being with me that unforgettable afternoon. They invited me to stop and visit them once in a while.

I knew I would miss them. I would miss all of the staff at St. John Lutheran Home. They were my friends. After all, it had been almost five years since Mom had entered St. John Lutheran Home.

Then I walked down the hallway carrying Mom's suitcase and her walking stick. I punched the button, and the elevator opened its door for me. In a few seconds, I was on first floor. I missed seeing Joan at the front desk; she didn't work on Sunday afternoons. I always chatted with her whenever I headed home. Before I walked through the automatic doors to the outside, I buttoned my coat, pulled my hood up, and put on my gloves. It was cold, and it was snowing.

When I got to my car, I opened the door and put Mom's suitcase and her walking stick in the back seat. I decided to give her walking stick to Tom, my youngest son, because he was the one who was with me the day we walked her into St. John Lutheran Home. I carefully laid the suitcase on the seat. It was snowing heavily now with big flakes, flakes that stuck to the windshield. I put on the wipers so I could see where I was going. It was hard to believe Mom was gone. It would take me awhile to feel it. I was numb. I couldn't cry.

As I drove the eight miles home, I thought about life and about death. What is life anyway? We're born. We live a little while. We die. The book of James says it better in James 4:14, "What is your life? You are a mist that appears for a little while and then vanishes." Life. A mist. A snowflake. That soon vanishes.

Mom's death would be in the obituary column in a few days, and it would not make the headlines. I thought about the number of people that die in just one day, and I considered the number of people that have ever lived and died. That number would be like counting the number of snowflakes.

The snowflakes were heavier now. My windshield wiper was getting clogged with the snow as I was driving along. The Bible says that the life and death of every person is significant to God. He has a plan and a time for every death because He is a God of order and a God of design. The snowflake, as tiny as it is, has an individual design. Mom's death was like a snowflake. Seemingly, the number seven was an element of the design. The number seven is God's number that means complete.

Strangely enough, it was about seven minutes from the time Mom smiled at her escort until the time she took her last shallow breath. The purple tide took around seven hours. We spent seven days in the valley of the shadow of death. Apparently, Mom's death had a design with the number seven. Seven minutes. Seven hours. Seven days.

As I turned the last corner to go home, I thought about Mom's lifetime in terms of a mist, a vapor that soon passes, like a tiny snowflake. I marveled at how quickly life goes even if a person lives to be almost ninety. As I drove down our gravel road to our home, I pictured Mom's lifetime as a tiny snowflake floating away, intricately designed with the number seven and artistically inscribed with her identity.

Remembering Mom
Chapter Twenty

Twenty years is a long time to be on a journey, especially one that has such a deep emotional impact. As Mom's journey with Alzheimer's finally ended when she died that Sunday afternoon, I wondered if I would ever be able to forget the mental image of Mom as she looked that afternoon. Would I ever be able to remember Mom as she was? Her appearance? Her personality? Since I was so closely involved with Mom in her decline and in her death, I had a lot to erase from my mind. I wondered if I could ever erase it. Would I always think of her as my Alzheimer's Mom?

Today, as I am putting the finishing touches on this chapter almost three years after Mom died, I can assure you I have found a way to forget what needs to be forgotten, and to remember what I want to remember about Mom. Admittedly, it took time for the bad mental images of Mom's condition to fade away. I had to work at creating a positive mental image of Mom to replace the bad one. In fact, I still keep working at it.

Here's how I deal with it. Over and over in my mind, I use the memory of Mom enjoying a dish of ice cream. It was just an ordinary moment in her life, but it was a happy moment. Thinking about Mom eating her sundae, that "moment of moments," brings special warmth inside of me because I can see her as she was. I can envision her appearance, her face, her eyes, and her smile. I can feel the warmth of her smile, and I can hear her voice as she says, "Mmmm . . . that was so good."

Butterscotch sundaes! Healing memories for me!

Directly after a loved one dies, a person tends to go through the motions of the funeral and burial services with a certain level of numbness. Later, the person feels all of the feelings. I was very thankful that my brother and I had taken the time and effort to plan for Mom's burial. We did this a year or so prior to her death, so when it actually happened, it was much easier for us. Naturally, we planned to bury Mom next to my father in a plot in Graceland Park Cemetery at Sioux City, Iowa. Why there? Why Sioux City? That was the spot that marked the end of my father's life journey when he died in 1974. Mom died in 2000. After twenty-six years of separation, in a sense they would be somewhat together again being buried side by side.

As far as planning the funeral service, I had the honor of doing it. With Mom's condition like it was, I had plenty of time to think and plan for it before it actually happened. Mom was a quiet, shy person; she would not have wanted anything elaborate. It had to be simple and private. I decided to have it at the funeral home in charge of her burial, the funeral home in Sioux City. I wanted it to be held in one of their small rooms because we didn't need a large facility. I knew it would be a small gathering of people. It would be my family and my brother's family, maybe a few of our friends.

When my brother and I had met to plan for her burial a year prior to her death, I visited the church in Sioux City where Mom and I were former members. Naturally, it had changed tremendously in thirty years. In the huge congregation of people, I barely found one couple who remembered us. The church had grown so much over the years, and it had been remodeled so many times that I could no longer recognize it. I knew then I would never plan to have Mom's funeral in a church that no longer remembered her, nor would I ask a minister who did not know her to be in charge of her funeral service.

Who then would I invite to give the sermon at our service at the funeral chapel? I wanted someone who knew Mom. Actually, I wanted someone who knew Mom before the Alzheimer's journey began. My best choice was a former pastor of ours who retired and lived in Odessa, Texas. But was that reasonable? Was it reasonable to ask him to come to Sioux

City for the service? I decided against that plan.

Who then would be in charge of the service? Who knew her? The answer was obvious. Her family knew her like no one else knew her. We could do it. We could hold a service that was private and simple, the kind of service that would honor her. We could make it a celebration of her life, of how she used to be before Alzheimer's took us all on the journey.

I must admit it was rather daring of me to plan a service without a church, without a pastor, without a sermon, without an organist, and without a soloist. I liked the idea of departing from the traditional kind of funeral because I like being creatively different. In fact, I became energized when I thought about having the informal gathering. It would be private and personal, just the way Mom would have wanted it to be.

What about having music at her service? Mom loved music. She loved to play her favorite old-fashioned hymns on her organ. How could we have music? No organ. No piano. No soloist. What could I do to have music? I decided to show a musical video, one produced by Reader's Digest.

I first discovered the video as I stopped to visit Mom one day. The residents were watching it as part of their activities program for the afternoon. I stood in the background and quietly observed Mom as she watched the video. She was pleased with it. The longer I watched it, the more I realized how much it was like her, almost tailored-made for her. The video was a beautiful combination of Mom's favorite hymns and her favorite scenes from God's creation. We saw geese flying, birds nesting, flowers blooming, horses climbing the mountains, deer grazing in meadows, and sailboats sailing into beautiful sunsets. Some of the hymns were instrumentals; others were sung by groups or by soloists.

I made a special point to find the owner of the video, who was a resident on Mom's floor. Shortly before Mom died, I went to the little woman who owned the video, and I asked her if I could borrow it for my mom's memorial service. She replied she would be honored to let me use it. Then I took the video to a friend to edit it to a shorter time frame, a half-hour instead of an hour. I picked Mom's favorite hymns to use for her service.

As I watched the edited version of the video, I realized that the video would make a perfect sermon. The words of each song would have a message for us that day, a message just as eloquent as any sermon could be. " What A Friend We Have In Jesus," "His Eye Is On The Sparrow," "In The Sweet By And By," and "Amazing Grace," would express words of comfort for us. Mom's faith would be evidenced through her favorite hymns, assuring us that she was in a better place.

My oldest son, Benton, would be in charge of the hour-long service. The first half hour would be our time of reminiscing about Mom; the second half hour would be our watching the musical video. After the service at the funeral chapel, we would travel by car to Graceland Park Cemetery for the burial. My son-in-law, Chad, would host the informal time at the gravesite. After the brief service, we planned to gather at my brother's farm for refreshments and for family togetherness for the rest of the day.

Besides planning her memorial service, I also spent time looking at old photos of Mom. I rearranged them by putting them in new albums. My intention was to take them to my brother's place for the special family gathering directly following the funeral. Seeing the photos of Mom would help our family to restore the mental image of what she used to be.

Planning for Mom's service was a rather strange but necessary thing for me to do as I sat by her side day after day while we going through the "valley of the shadow of death." I am grateful that we had time to plan for Mom's funeral and burial. It made it a lot easier for my brother and me to get through the painful experience. When it's your mom, it's your mom and no one else's mom. It hurts.

There is beauty in simplicity. Mom's funeral service was simple and private. Less than thirty people, mostly family attended that February day. My son Benton did a good job of hosting the event. One by one, he introduced family members, inviting them to come to the podium to share their impressions and memories of Mom as she used to be. Nothing was mentioned about her Alzheimer's condition. Instead, we focused on the positive memories as we fondly remembered her.

Then, as we watched the video, it seemed as if Mom were giving the sermon that day. Her Christian witness, her faith, and her assurance of eternal life were so evident in the words of her favorite hymns being performed for us, as we watched colorful scenes set in perfect harmony with the music.

Finally, my son closed the service in prayer. As family and friends made their way outside to the parking lot, my brother and I lingered by the open casket. For a moment we stood together, just the two of us, to take our last look at our mother. In that quiet moment, we celebrated the woman who had given us life, who had taught us her values, and who had consistently prayed for us. For a short time, we gazed at the little white-haired woman lying there so peacefully with her pink nail polish on her fingernails. In our hearts we saluted her with our last look. Then we walked away wiping a few tears from our eyes.

The funeral director gently closed the casket, and the casket bearers escorted it outside to be put in the hearse. Only a few cars followed the hearse as it made its way across town to the cemetery. It took about twenty minutes to get there. Graceland Park is a huge cemetery; a person actually needs a map to find the right pathway to visit someone's grave.

As we paused at the entrance gate waiting for the rest of the cars to catch up with us, I looked at the words etched across the archway, Graceland Park. I marveled at the name of the cemetery. Mom's journey was finally over. We were now at the ultimate destination. The journey had been long, but it was a journey of grace, God's marvelous, day-by-day, moment-by-moment kind of grace. Graceland Park was a fitting name for her final resting place.

Just a handful of people stepped inside the tent the funeral home had provided for us at the gravesite. As I stood there, waiting for our humble service to begin, I couldn't help but remember the spring day when we buried my father in the same spot. It was a sunny day in May. The grass was green on the knoll of the tiny hill where a single tree provided shade for us as we stood together for the burial service. Now the grass was snow covered. Nothing looked the same.

When everyone had gathered inside the funeral tent, the service began. My son-in-law, Chad, called our attention to the words of inscription on my parent's gravestone. He mentioned the words, Thy Will Be Done, and he reminded everyone that twenty-six years had passed since my father had been laid to rest in that very spot. His other comments were brief.

Just as I requested earlier, Chad sang the beautiful and timeless hymn, "The Lord's Prayer." He sang with confidence, with no music to accompany him. The words were powerful as they punctured the eerie silence of the cemetery on that cold, wintry day. Chad's voice was loud and strong as each word filled the expanse of the graveyard. When Chad came to the final words, his voice was overflowing with praise. The words echoed throughout the cemetery, almost dancing across the gravestones covered with ice and snow. "For thine... is the Kingdom... and the power... and the glory... forever... Amen." When he finished with a final and awesome "Amen," there was an appropriate time of silence followed by a prayer that signaled the close of the service.

There is beauty in simplicity.

Now that Mom is gone, we miss her, and we think of her often. Russell and I continue to remember Mom in our own personal ways. "When it's your mother, no matter how long you have her with you, you still miss her." Russell told me he misses her when he goes in his pickup truck, whether it's to town for parts, to the pasture to check the cattle, or to fix the fences. He misses seeing her sitting beside him smiling and enjoying the ride.

In the springtime, Russell thinks of her when he sees the cherry tree blossoms. He remembers her good cherry pies that she always baked for him. When he's fixing fence in the pasture and he walks among the wild plum trees growing there, he remembers her picking plums in her pail and later making them into jelly for him.

On certain days as he walks by the south side of his house, he pictures her sitting in her lawn chair taking what she called a sunbath, with the cats and dogs sitting beside her. He easily recalls how her beautiful white hair glistened in the sun.

For me, remembering Mom is an on-going thing. I see her when I see the sunset from my kitchen window, as the sun slowly sinks behind the pine trees behind our house.

I feel her near me when I walk the prairie, especially when I am wearing her summer jacket. I think of her whenever the geese are flying over us in the fall and in the spring.

When I bake old-fashioned molasses cookies on a Sunday afternoon or whenever I use her favorite recipe for chocolate cake, pumpkin pie, or strawberry jam, I think of her. If I am feeling low, I play her favorite hymns on my CD player. Then I find her Bible, and I read her handwritten notes in the margins by her favorite verses, and I look at the poems and clippings that she saved between the pages.

Whenever I see a woman with beautiful white hair and a warm friendly smile, I think of Mom. Once when I was walking in a shopping mall, I saw a woman that looked like her. For a moment, I thought, "Oh, there's Mom," but then, I knew it couldn't be her.

I still have Mom's favorite mug in my kitchen. She didn't drink coffee; she drank tea. Sometimes she drank what she called "frog wine," just plain hot water. I wish now that I would have asked Mom why she called it frog wine. I guess I always thought she'd be there to answer that question for me. So, I never asked her.

For my brother and for me, remembering Mom will always be a part of our lives. In fact, thoughts of her can happen at any time of the day or night. Sometimes, it happens at an "out of the blue" moment, like when we're at the Dairy Queen, and someone standing near us orders a butterscotch sundae.

Life Goes On
Chapter Twenty One

It's springtime! Graduation 2001 time! Yesterday, my son Tom brought home his high school graduation cap and gown, an eye-catching bright blue, not a dignified black, like the cap and gown worn by my oldest son a few months ago when he got his degree as a chiropractor.

In the winter of 2000, Mom graduated when her earthly existence ended, and she started her heavenly one, leaving behind the legacy of her Alzheimer's journey. In the process of writing her story, I have grieved, I have laughed, and I have cried. As I write this final chapter, I am feeling triumphant at last. Admittedly, I will be doing lots of revising in the future before it actually goes to press. But today, I can say that I have come to the end of this book.

Whenever we finish a journey, sooner or later we realize that the journey left its mark upon us. It changed us! We know that we are different, much different from when we began the journey. We know that we can't go back. We wouldn't want to go back. We must go forward. Life goes on!

Life is a journey; there's no doubt about it. We don't know how long our journey will last. Mom's lasted for nearly ninety years. My father's lasted for sixty-five years. No one really knows the exact number of our days or of our years. The most important thing in life is to know about death. When the journey is over, where we will spend eternity?

Now that our mom and dad are both gone, it's rather humbling for my brother and me to realize we are the older generation. We are the grandparents now. We are the "Nana" and the "Papa" for our grandkids. That puts our children in the "middle of the sandwich." Things have changed for everyone.

Recently I read these words on a refrigerator magnet, "Be kind to your children, they choose the nursing home." My children already know that my wishes are to go to St. John Lutheran Home, when and if that time comes, because I want "the pink nail polish" kind of care.

Whenever I visit St. John Lutheran Home, I see the changes, or I learn about them from Joan at the front desk. Mary Krueger is the new administrator. Riverhaven has been established as an Alzheimer's unit designed to meet the needs of Alzheimer's people. Chaplain Mary is extremely happy with the newly completed Chapel of the Good Shepherd. And Parker, the Irish setter, is on a diet. He has gained too much weight with handouts and too many sneaky snacks.

When I walk the hallway where Mom once lived, I see different names on the nameplates. Most of Mom's friends are no longer there. Her roommate Marie died shortly after Mom died. Grace is gone now. Viola is gone, too. Everything changes. But life goes on.

Our dog Katie is heading for 90 in human years. Our entry way is the nursing home for a very special dog. She has her own comforter, water dish, and food dish beside her. Aside from her occasional visits outdoors, she is content to stay put on her quilt and sleep and sleep and sleep.

My husband Stan is famous for his sod house dream because he was recently filmed for a new documentary for the History Channel, called "Frontier Homes," which is part of their award winning series, "Save Our History." Sometimes, life brings a flash of fame.

Now that my husband and I are in our fifty's, we are finding the fabulous fifty's to be less than fabulous because health problems sometimes surface. Before Christmas, I had a mammogram, and then I got a phone call I didn't like hearing. "We found something on your mammogram, and we need some more views and an ultrasound. Come in the Wednesday after Christmas." Ultimately, I had surgery to remove a suspicious lump. Finally, our family got the diagnosis, the one we wanted to hear. "No cancer cells found."

My husband had been having some problems so he also had some tests done. Sadly enough, before Christmas we got my husband's diagnosis, the one our family didn't want to hear. He has Parkinson's disease. Now our family is taking another journey, one that we would not choose to take. Life is never what we plan it to be. We have to take the bitter with the sweet. Having just learned that lesson, we will trust God for this new journey. Will He disappoint us? I don't think so.

Tom's graduation time will soon be here. My mother-in-law, Phyllis, and I will make the graduation cakes. She will arrive at our place on the Thursday before the Sunday graduation, bringing with her the cake mixer, cake pans, and cake recipe. We will bake enough graduation cake to serve around a hundred people. Then my daughter, Christy, and my daughter-in-law, Heidi, will decorate the cakes to give them that special graduation look.

Mom will not be with us for Tom's graduation day, and I will miss her. Of course, I will think of her as we celebrate that day. In fact, I have a beautiful memory of her enjoying my son Charlie's graduation party. She was smiling as she stood by the punch bowl and chatted with everyone who came by her that day. Her brown eyes sparkled as she held her glass of punch and as she ate her cake and ice cream. Thankfully, that wonderful memory was captured by camera, and that snapshot is on the front cover of this book.

Mom is gone now, but Mom's family lives on. Three generations of her family will be having fun together on graduation day, especially when it's time to make the punch. My little granddaughter, Mariah, will be standing on a chair next to the table so she can watch her mother pour the sour fruit juice into the big glass punch bowl. I will add plenty of sugar and ginger ale to make it taste sweet. No doubt, we will be smiling at something cute that only a two-year-old can say. Mariah's dark brown eyes will dance with delight when she takes the big spoon and stirs the punch.

Then it's taste time! More sugar? More fruit juice? More ginger ale? Then it's taste time again! Too sweet? Too sour? Too flat? Just right!

Life goes on. Sometimes it's bitter. Sometimes it's sweet. Sometimes it's bittersweet. It always changes. It never stays the same. Yes, life goes on!

St. John Lutheran Home   Springfield, Minnesota

Mom was a gracious person. She would want to thank everyone at St. John Lutheran Home. The cleaning lady, the janitor, the kitchen crew, the dietician, the laundry crew, the social workers, the Pastor, the Chaplain, the volunteers, the activities department, St. John GrandKids, the doctor, the nurses and the nurse aides. On behalf of Mom, thank you everyone! You are greatly appreciated!

The "pink nail polish" kind of care that Mom experienced at St. John Lutheran Home prompts me to acknowledge her personal caregivers by their names. Thank you! Bless you!

[The following names were taken from her medical chart.]

Nurse Aides

Denise Gicker, Tricia Suess, Darla Knutson, Lisa Goblirsch, Krista Voge, Becky Sawatzky, Michael Nachreiner, Tiffini Sturm, Jill Evers, Shareen Halvorson, Amanda Olson, Jami Niemann, Katie Maurer, Gretchen Dauer, Kristin Erickson, Jenny Erickson, Jan Erickson, Sara Lewis, Cassie Plotz, Eric Schwarzrock, Mary Groebner, Nicole Hillesheim, Rita Nachreiner, Jennifer Kirchoff, Jess Woelfel, Joan Hoffman, Amanda Otto, Joyce Schwarzrock, Deb Schumacher, Rita Bell, Jenni Juve, Jennifer Heilman, Millie Brown, Molly Krieg, Jean Halvorson, Cora Weber, Missy Mude, Kathleen Woychick,

Andrew Landkammer, Dustin VanOverbeke, Ronda Luck, Jamie Jensen, Gianna Anderson, Pat Benson, Jill Dehn, Christie Braun, Kay Matter, Trisha Groebner, Cathy Berberich, Carolyn Shandy, Maria Therkelsen, Shari Anderson, Bonnie Brand, Krista Davis, Mandy Hillesheim, Dawn Roiger, Brenda Kotten

TMA's
Jodi Streich, Dianna Basballe, Trisha Groebner, Elizabeth Gewerth, Anne Wersal, Sue Flor, Stacy Platz, Chris Gatzlaff, Gina Hammerschmidt, Dee Dee Leopold, LeAnn Jensen, Cora Schmidt, Shari Roiger, Jami Niemann, Doreen Christensen, Mary Simonson, Jolene Schenk, Lisa Vogel, Jan Anderson, Mary Vogel, Linda Gartner, Liza Streich, JoAnn Schwartz, Barb Haugen, Michelle Thompson, Clare Nelson, Mindy Ryan, Jodi Nachreiner, Meggan Sturm, Krista Davis, Kristen Hurias, Alisa Krieg

LPN's and RN's
Cindy Wellner, Danita Evans, Sharon Pankonin, Caryn Randall, Marian Jensen, Ruth Fults, Dorothy Almer, Jennifer Rempel, Sara Rogotzke, Caryn Bommersbach, Kathy Hillesheim, Heather Rogotzke, Ardis Nielsen, Lu Ann Hemmingsen, Michelle Thompson, Rhonda Utz, Terri Mathiowetz, Sharyn Sullivan, Wendy Sawatzky, Sara Schmitz, Mary Krebs Vicki Wendt, Jo Ann Briesath, Mary Mathiowitz,

We would like to especially thank Mary Krebs, Sara Schmitz, Vicki Wendt, Chaplain Mary Pauluk, Dr. Michael Schmitz, Marlys Garnes, Jill Dehn, Pat Benson, Linda Gartner, Jan Anderson, Jodi Streich, Dustin Van Overbeck, Katie Maurer, Joan Hoffman, Christine Jacoby, and Brenna Thompson. Thanks to all the volunteers who read to her, sang to her, and prayed with her.

When names are named, there is a chance of someone being forgotten. Thank you, our unnamed hero! We appreciate you, too. Please write your name on this page!

A Family Effort!

I would especially like to thank my sister-in-law, Anne, for her many years of tender loving care for Mom. Her devotion was just as intense for my mom as it was for her own dear mother. Thank you Anne for being a remarkable caregiver. Bless you!

Thank you Mike, Mark and Connie! You were wonerful to her!

I also appreciate my aunt Lois for being Mom's caregiver for four years while she lived in Colorado. Thank you, Lois! Mom was blessed to be able to spend that time with you, and with her brother and sister.

A special thanks to my husband and my children for your help and support during the last seven years of Mom's life. I couldn't have done it without you!

My deepest gratitude goes to my brother, Russell! Thank you for gathering Mom under your wing after Dad died. You made a home for her with you, and you honored her every request. Your loyalty is most commendable. Bless you!

* * * *

Russell	Stan	Lois
Anne	Virginia	Tom
Mike	Christy	Mabel
Mark	Benton	
Connie	Charlie	
	Steve	
	Tom	

Bausch   McCone   Brompton

2000 Photo

To my little granddaughter, Mariah,
thank you
for giving us precious insights.

By being so natural,
spontaneous, playful and imaginative,
you teach us
how to relate to the elderly.

A red barn on the Pitman farm?

Mom and I often went for a ride together to ease her agitation. Her mind was living in another place and in another time zone. Her obsession to find the Pitman farm of Lake Villa, Illinois, was typical of the wandering stage of Alzheimer's. She would say to me, "It's so simple. It's just over that hill. Keep driving. We'll get to the Pitman farm. You'll see."

Recommendation:
Whatever you do, play along with them.
Meet them where they are but always on pleasant terms.

To learn more about creating special moments, I highly recommend Jolene Brackey's book entitled, *Creating Moments of Joy for the Person with Alzheimer's or Dementia.*

Actual purse belonging to Mom's mother, Jesse Pitman Brompton.

You can contact Jolene at www.enhancedmoments.com or write to Jolene at Enhanced Moments, P.O. Box 383, Polk City, IA 50226.

Come Visit Me is a pocket-sized booklet written by Virginia McCone that teaches how to visit the elderly, especially a person in a nursing home or assisted living.

Each page has a practical suggestion of how to enrich your visit. Simply written, this is a real "how to" booklet.

You can contact Virginia at www.sodhouse.org or write to her at Autumn Sparrow Press, 12589 Magnolia Avenue, Sanborn, MN 56083.

Mom's doll, her companion from 1998-2000.

Her brown eyes sparkle when she tastes the butterscotch topping. Each spoonful is savored. She scrapes the sides and bottom of the dish. Then she dabs the corner of each side of her mouth with her napkin and smiles as she says in her low soothing voice, "Mmm... that was so good."

1915 Photo

Ethel Mae Brompton Bausch

1910-2000

Life. A mist. A snowflake. That soon vanishes.

Make the most of the present moment.
When it's gone, it's gone.

* * * Virginia McCone